MW00658976

Priceless CAREGIVING

STORIES *of* ELDER CARE SUCCESS, COURAGE *and* STRENGTH

Compiled *by* Valerie VanBooven RN BSN

LTC Expert Publications, LLC • St. Charles, Missouri

PRICELESS CAREGIVING:
STORIES OF ELDER CARE SUCCESS, COURAGE AND STRENGTH

First printing 2009

Published by: LTC Expert Publications, LLC
St. Charles, Missouri
PHONE: 877.529.0550
EMAIL: *Valerie@theltcexpert.com*
WEBSITE: *www.theltcexpert.com*

ISBN: 978-0-9825980-0-9

Cover Design and Interior Design © TLC Graphics, *www.tlcgraphics.com*
Cover design: Monica Thomas; Interior Design: Erin Stark

Printed and bound by Bang Printing, Brainerd, Minnesota

Dedications

THIS BOOK IS DEDICATED TO ADULT CHILDREN OF AGING PARENTS, CAREGIVERS, seniors, and people who are tireless advocates of the elderly, and quality long-term care. The business owners, caregivers, and families who helped contribute to the creation of this book are the real heroes. They are the ones who care for our aging adults without fail, every day. Without these heroes, growing older wouldn't be so much fun.

There are those of you who no longer have a voice—we, as caregivers, are proud to have served as your advocates and your protectors in a time of need.

For those of you who still have a voice, keep expressing, keep advocating, and keep reaching out and educating others.

From you, I learn something new every day. To my family, friends, and loved ones, thank you for your patience, your support, your encouragement, and your influence. I do believe that anything is possible. To my husband Charles Lee Whitsell and my children the triplets—Madeline Anne Whitsell, Sophia Belle Whitsell, and Samantha Lee Whitsell, born 3/05/2007, thank you for everything, you make life wonderful!

Table of Contents

Dedications iii

Foreword ix

Smoke Gets In Your Eyes
by Evelyn Praul 1

My Mother's Story Becomes Our Professional Passion and Destiny
by Ken & Roberta Labart 4

Girls Will Be Girls!
by Beth Sholom 6

Lessons from Holocaust Survivors
by Beth Sholom 8

Mom's Hip
by Evelyn Praul 10

The Capacity to Love Our Clients
by Robert Jo, CSA 12

Finding the Right Caregiver Through Right At Home
by Joe & Allison Bakey 14

First Contact, First Client
by Kelly Reventar 16

I Promise
by Ken & Roberta Labart 20

It's a Better Life for Betty
by Mark Stowers 22

Just to Hear My Grandchildren's Voices
by Mark Stowers 24

A Love Story
by Marla Beck 26

What Goes Around
by Marlan J. Holland 28

Learning to Listen from the Heart
by Mary Chapa, RN 30

Mavis Lindgren, Grandma Wears Running Shoes
by Patrick Roden, RN, PhD 32

Connecting With Others Enriches Seniors' Lives
by Stephanie Weiger 35

Caring for Aunt Florence
by Terry Garcia 37

From Tragedy to Triumph
by Rosaleen & Jay Kenney 39

A Tale of Two Sisters
by David A. Travland, PhD & Rhonda Travland 41

The Widowed Mother and Her Son: Who is Caring for Whom?
by Patrick Roden, PhD 44

Sports and Son Saved Dad
by Bill Ranieri 47

It's All About the Cookies
by Ron Hagberg, CSA & Susan Green, RN, CSA 49

A Comforting Solution
by Sandra Desjardins 51

Thanksgiving Day 1990
by Sue Ansari, RN 53

Just the Two of Us
by Randi Walden 56

A Tribute to My Dad
by Robert Jo, CSA 58

In Our Home—My Mother's Choice
by Barbara Roden 60

What a Difference the Right Caregiver Makes
by Laurie Saunders 62

Enhancing the Quality of Life
by Laurie Saunders 64

Lessons Learned from Nana
by Shari Westman 66

Personal Story of Alice Silversby
by Stephen P. Rudolph, FACHE, CSA 69

When One Door Closes, Another Opens
by Warren Miller 71

Reverse Mortgages—Real Life Solutions for Senior Homeowners
by Sue Haviland 73

On a Mission for Uncle John
by Barbara Roden 75

Independence for Life
by Barbara Roden 77

Francine's Life Has Changed
by Sheila Korn 79

A Place for Evangeline
by Marcie Jones 81

Good for Families
by Marcie Jones 83

What In-Home Care Giving Really Should Be for Your Loved One
by Beth Bates 85

Mr. Lloyd's Favorite Visitor
by Riki Sopher 88

My Guardian Angel
by Lisa Marie Blaskie, RN, CCM, CSA 90

My Mom: On the Wings of Angels
by Paula Camposano-Robinson RN 92

I'll Never Forget You
by Meghan Shea 96

PRICELESS CAREGIVING
RESOURCES AND INFORMATION 83

Choosing Home Care Services
by Valerie VanBooven, RN, BSN 101

Adult Day Services
by Valerie VanBooven, RN, BSN 103

Hiring a Geriatric Care Manager (Elder Care Manager)
by Valerie VanBooven, RN, BSN 105

When the Caregiver Needs a Break...Where Can They Turn?
by Valerie VanBooven, RN, BSN 109

Pay Yourself or a Loved One for Providing Care—
The Options and Tax Benefits
by Valerie VanBooven, RN, BSN 113

Choosing Independent Senior Living,
Assisted Living, and Nursing Home Care
by Valerie VanBooven, RN, BSN 117

Resources Online and Offline
by Valerie VanBooven, RN, BSN 121

Foreword

I AM CONSTANTLY AMAZED BY THE NEVER ENDING SELFLESSNESS OF PEOPLE IN the business of caregiving. Every business owner who took the time to write one, two or three stories for this book are living proof that angels exist on Earth. These people and their staff members do jobs that most of us couldn't even begin to imagine. The rewards for them are joyous and overwhelming. The families (names changed) in this book are shining examples of people who came together to do the right thing for their aging loved one.

Family caregivers are often stressed out, overwhelmed, tired and worried. The professionals who enter their lives pick up the pieces and put it all back together. Even more heartwarming are the stories from the owners of these businesses who have a very personal reason for owning a home care agency, an assisted living facility, adult day care, or nursing home. They've been where you are today. They have been through what most adult children sort of secretly hope they never have to face…caring for an aging parent.

Not only did the contributors of this book experience family caregiving first hand, they went on to care for others in their own communities. If you are reading this book, my guess is that an angel handed it to you. Be sure to keep that angel around to help you and your family. These are the people who have such passion for helping families, they took the time to write it all down.

Enjoy!

VALERIE VANBOOVEN RN BSN

Author of *The Senior Solution: A Family Guide to Keeping Seniors Home for Life* 2007, and the author of *Aging Answers: Secrets to Successful Long-Term Care Planning, Caregiving, and Crisis Management* 2003.

ALL FOR YOU HOME CARE
777 Campus Commons Road, Suite 200
Sacramento, CA 95825
PHONE: 916.479.8554
TOLL-FREE: 877.690.4003
FAX: 916.929.0448
EMAIL: *allforyouhomecare@gmail.com*

Smoke Gets In Your Eyes

by EVELYN PRAUL

ONE DAY BOB AND I WENT TO DINNER WHERE A SMALL COMBO WAS PLAYING old time classic tunes. Bob wanted to dance. That's why he, his trusty walker, and I, moved slowly to the dance floor. All three of us swayed back and forth to "Smoke gets in Your Eyes." Bob couldn't complete the dance but the smile on his face was as if he had danced all night.

My name is Marti and I am a caregiver. For me, caregiving is more than a career. It is my passion. When I first met Bob he was just out of the hospital. He had fallen, hit his head and suffered a small concussion. Although he would soon heal from the fall, he could not heal from the degenerative disease that was taking its toll on him. So, when I first met Bob I began to explore how I could best help him at this point in his life.

The more I got to know Bob, the more I realized that in addition to his physical ailments, Bob was suffering from depression. It was as if he had given up and got very little pleasure from his life. I decided that Bob needed me, to help restore fun and adventure to his life. I knew that this would be a challenge since Bob was limited in his physical abilities. I hoped that my cheerful positive attitude could help change his life for the better. After all, smiles are hard to resist.

Throughout his life Bob had loved playing golf. Now, due to his limited physical ability, he could no longer play golf. I, on the other hand, had never played golf but had always been interested in learning more about the game. One day we were talking about playing golf and before I knew it I found myself on the golf course. Bob, with his new found spirit was leaning on his walker showing me how to hold the golf club. I was trying to hit the balls. We probably looked strange to others as they passed, but for us, it was a wonderful adventure. We could not care less about what others thought. So, this was the beginning of Bob and my daily adventures.

We discovered that the simplest of daily activities could be fun. Whenever we were in the car and needed gas, I would insist that Bob buy a lottery ticket. One time, low and behold, he won $10. We celebrated as if he had won a million dollars.

I realized that Bob liked to watch classic movies. So, one day I took him to the video store and convinced him to get his own card. We would go to the store and he would spend an hour looking through old movies. He would pick a few and he would check them out. We would enjoy watching the movies while eating dinner. For us, this became more than checking out movies, it became another small activity that became a fun tradition.

Probably for most of us, going to the doctor is not an adventure. On a particularly good day, however, Bob suggested that it would be fun to eat at a restaurant near the doctor's office. Soon, whenever we would go to the doctor's office, we would go to eat at this same restaurant. This became our own personal tradition—a tradition that we both looked forward to doing together. Now going to the doctor took on a whole new meaning—it was one of our personal adventures.

Once Bob became interested in the small things we were doing to have fun, we became partners in this effort. Bob came to trust me. The kind of trust that built character for both him and me. Together, we filled the days with good times. You see, one of the things that Bob needed most was the care that lifted his spirit. What I discovered was that the same small adventures that Bob enjoyed, also lifted my spirit. Bob and I became true partners in adventure.

I know that at the end of my days that I will look back at my life and know I made a difference in the lives of others. This is why I am a caregiver.

Recently when I was thinking about my time with Bob, I turned my car radio to one of his favorite stations. As I listened I heard the familiar sounds of "Smoke Gets in Your Eyes." It took me back to those days with Bob and how we had found ways to turn the simplest of life's activities into wonderful adventures. I listened carefully to the lyrics at the end:

Tears I cannot hide
Oh, so I smile and say
When a lovely flame dies
Smoke gets in your eyes
Smoke gets in your eyes.
Bob was a lovely flame.

BERKEN SENIOR CARE, LLC
2300 McDermott, Suite 200-296
Plano, Texas 75025
PHONE: 214.808.2006
EMAIL: *Ken@berkenseniorcare.com*
EMAIL: *Roberta@berkenseniorcare.com*

My Mother's Story Becomes Our Professional Passion and Destiny

by KEN & ROBERTA LABART

THE DAY HAD FINALLY ARRIVED WHEN A BELOVED FAMILY MEMBER HAD BECOME dependent upon assistance from someone beyond themselves. We all think about it from time to time, but we never seem to be completely ready, when it actually arrives. There are just so many different directions one must review during this time, all to ensure you have a plan in place that will provide that smooth transition.

That day did indeed come to me when my mother's health took an unexpected turn, and I was faced with a day of enormous decisions. I was one of two siblings, and being her oldest son, whom she knew would take the lead to ensure her comfort and her affairs, that she would be in good hands. My wife and I lived several hundred miles from the small community where my mother lived, and I grew up. My wife and I are involved in professional careers and sometimes with schedules that overwhelmed our individual lives. My younger sister lived in the same small community as my mother, but with her and her husband also having very busy schedules, it left little time to provide the assistance and care that my mother expected and truly deserved. My sister and I both promised my mother we would ensure her care, and live up to my mother's request to continue for her to live at her own home for the remaining of her days. We had a huge challenge in front of us.

The biggest obstacle we had was identifying a home care agency to assist us initially, with simple companionship. We began our search through every method and means we could think of, but to no avail. The community was small and in a rural setting, so our resources were very limited. We looked online, the local yellow pages, the newspaper classifieds, and local churches. We talked to the local hospital and found that they offered hospice services, but didn't provide companion or caregiver care. We looked into an independent individual, but what we found sometimes made us a little nervous. We became disappointed in our findings. My sister and I were faced with some very difficult decisions.

Our process took numerous turns, with tremendous anxiety and sleepless nights. My sister and I had many telephone conversations together, trying to strategize and plan our approach. As our options continued to fade, we finally were faced with the decision that one of us would need to make a sacrifice with our career, to assist in the care and comfort of our mother. My wife and I decided that I would be the sibling that would assume the role of primary caregiver to my beloved mother. It was a difficult and bitter sweet decision. I have been involved as an executive in the business industry my entire life, and was a little nervous to take on a role so much different than I've been so accustom to. Initially the care was primarily non medical and simple companionship, so the commitment to her was fairly easy. However that gradually changed and her care became a little more involved, a little more demanding, and for all practical purposes, a 24 hour vigilance.

As the days and weeks followed my sister also made the decision to set her career on hold and actively involve herself in the care of our incredible mother. We began to feel an incredible sense of pride and purpose, and a deeper love for not only my mother, but a passion for care of our senior community. As corny and insincere as it may sound, we truly believe we found our calling to assist, care, and comfort our senior community. My wife and I began our company with all the passion, dedication, commitment, and compassion that reflected my mother's life long philosophy. For my wife and I, it began as a personal journey and became our professional destiny.

BETH SHOLOM
43 West Prospect St., Suite 204
East Brunswick, NJ 08816
PHONE: 732.967.0900
FAX: 732.967.0913
EMAIL: *rahcnj@verizon.net*
STATE LICENSE NUMBER: #HP0052100

Girls Will Be Girls!

by BETH SHOLOM

IT IS THE END OF AUGUST AND ONE OF MY MAJOR OBJECTIVES IS TO GET MY back-to-school shopping accomplished for my three children. After all Labor Day and the start of school are just around the corner.

I was in our local mall with my daughter this past weekend shopping at Abercrombie, Nordstrom, Victoria Secret, Steve Madden and other popular trendy stores. My daughter is 12 years old and going into the 7th grade. According to her, there are certain items she just “has to have.” We bumped into her friends in the food court and they all compared their recent purchases and showed each other everything in their respective shopping bags. Whatever they each did not have prompted a trip back to the stores as they all needed the same things.

This shopping experience coincided in its timing with my signing up a new client for Right at Home, the homecare company that I own with my husband.

On Monday, I signed up “Sally” for companion services to be provided several days per week. Her daughter, “Robin” was in town and she expressed to me that she was so relieved that she found Right at Home and that her Mom was going to have a companion helping her. Robin felt that she could return to her home, which was in another state, with a burden lifted off her shoulders, knowing that Mom would be well cared for, just in time for back to school.

As the hours of service we were planning on providing were just a few per day, I suggested that Mom purchase a life line button that I could install for her on another day. Sally and Robin both agreed. Well, I went back on Wednesday and heard about how much they both loved my caregiver as she had started working the evening before.

However, it is what happened on Tuesday afternoon that pulled on my heart strings. Robin told me how she and her Mom took a drive to "the old neighborhood." There, they ran into an old friend who is now 92 herself. Robin assisted this woman over to her car so that she could say hello to Sally. She guided her, with her walker, over to the car. The first thing that Sally said to her friend was "I have the same walker." Next, she asked her about the charm around her neck. The woman replied by saying it was a life line button. Sally excitedly exclaimed, "I am getting one tomorrow!" The conversation continued and they spoke about how they were both getting along. The 92-year-old woman expressed that she has a caregiver who helps her each day to shower and to get dressed. Sally delightfully replied that she too has a caregiver helping her.

So back to the beginning of my story—girls will be girls—whether you are 12 or 92, girls need the same things as their girlfriends. It may be something you just "have to have" or something you really "have to have," girls can always compare what's in "their shopping bags."

BETH SHOLOM
43 West Prospect St., Suite 204
East Brunswick, NJ 08816
PHONE: 732.967.0900
FAX: 732.967.0913
EMAIL: *rahcnj@verizon.net*
STATE LICENSE NUMBER: #HP0052100

Lessons from Holocaust Survivors

by BETH SHOLOM

WORLD WAR II ENDED ON AUGUST 8, 1945. THE PRISONERS OF AUSCHWITZ and other concentration camps were now free. What kind of a life did they have to look forward to at that point without their parents, spouses, children or siblings? Many of those now "free" were welcomed by the United States. Many ended up living in New Jersey and they tried to put the past behind them. They tried to find family members, they re-married, they had children and many had grandchildren and great grandchildren. Of course, they never forgot the misery and torture they experienced. Most never spoke about it.

Sixty four years later, many of those once young men and women are now seniors living in Middlesex County, New Jersey. This is the area that I serve in providing home care services through my business, Right at Home. Some of these holocaust survivors just need a little help whereas some have diminished mental capacity and unfortunately this causes them to relive the horrors and suffering of the early 1940's. Whatever their assistance requirement may be, Jewish Family and Vocational Services has established a grant wherein some of the needed services can be paid for. I, as the owner of Right at Home, have the honor of providing the much need services. I am very proud to be one of the providers of service to this group of clients. When they call my office and I hear their Yiddish accents, my heart melts and I cannot deny them any request they may have. We are not a cleaning service, but when Mrs. B. calls and tells me that she saved $60.00 and would like her companion to come in and extra day to clean (outside of the grant), I just put it on the schedule. Another client, Mr. D. just wants someone to cook him a decent meatloaf. Yet, another holocaust grant client is tormented by her past.

I thought long and hard when asked to write this article about which of these clients or any of our clients that I could write a story about to express how my company has impacted their lives. I realized that my company and my incredible staff make a difference every day in the lives of all of the clients we serve regardless of the level of care or the amount of care we provide. I realized that the life that has been most impacted is my own as I have the privilege of helping to make the daily life of all of my clients better, in particular, my many holocaust survivor clients. My grandparents would be so proud of me if they knew that I am helping to make the end of life for so many tortured souls, more dignified, more pleasant, more joyful and more secure.

We in the United States should be all the more thankful
for the freedom and religious tolerance we enjoy.
And we should always remember the lessons learned
from the Holocaust, in hopes we stay vigilant
against such inhumanity now and in the future.

CHARLIE DENT

Mom's Hip

by EVELYN PRAUL

THE NEW DOCTOR KNOCKED ON THE DOOR AND ENTERED THE EXAM ROOM holding Mom's medical chart. Somewhat confused he looked at me and quizzed "Who are you?" Before I could respond and explain that I was her daughter-in-law, Mom jumped right in and exclaimed, "She's my hip!" The doctor laughed. With just a few words she took charge of the conversation and changed the whole mood in the room. So, this is when I first became her hip.

The doctor said that Mom had cancer. From this time forward no matter how many doctors she saw, no matter how many treatments she received, no matter how much pain she endured, she always announced in a light hearted way that I was her hip. Doctors would laugh. Nurses would laugh. Other patients would laugh. She took dour and dark waiting rooms and turned them positive, and playful if only for a few minutes. I said to myself "Even in your darkest hours you took charge of the hospital in a manner that almost demanded laughter from others. No one ever again questioned my role. I was her hip because she said so. I knew that when she called me her hip she was saying that no matter what happened she could count on me, her daughter-in-law, to stand by her side. Nothing could have honored me more. A woman who had stood on her own throughout her life was saying that she trusted me with her greatest valuable—her life.

Over the next year, Mom faced chemo therapy, radiation, heart surgery and more treatments than I could ever have imagined. As doctors, poked, prodded, pulled, and pushed every way possible she maintained her dignity and her pride as much as possible. Why should I have been surprised. After all, this is how she had lived her whole life. As hard as it became, I would never have given up my assignment as her hip.

Mom had always been stronger and different from the crowd. She was a professional dancer who danced her last performance at age 70. Her husband had died when she was still young and she was left to raise 4 children as a single parent in a time when women had far fewer opportunities than today. With so little money and so many kids, she had to work long hours to feed her family.

The cancer progressed and the treatments gave her very little relief. I remain mystified how she walked down the aisle at her granddaughter's wedding. By this time she was having a very difficult time walking at all. Here she was walking down the aisle in front of over one hundred guests. She was wearing one of her beautiful gowns, her hair was styled to perfection and her makeup was applied with care. After the ceremony, she sat surrounded by guests and glowing as she was took her rightful role as the bride's grandmother. She made sure that few in the room had any idea how ill she was.

Finally, she decided to let my husband and me move into her one bedroom apartment so we could give her the help she had to have. Until this point, as sick as she was, she was determined to live on her own. Even now, she would not accept visitors unless she was "made-up." After all, she wanted to be remembered for her best. We would wheel her outside for long walks and talks. In this time we shared so many things together—how much I had learned about myself, about my priorities, about my health, about the past and about the future. We laughed and we cried.

I was always asking Mom what could we do to make her more comfortable. She would say, just promise me you will let me stay at home surrounded by my things and the people I love. Well that was a promise that we could make. That was a promise that we could keep. With all of the things that came our way, this is the one thing that was in our control.

I was laying next to her, and even in her weakened condition she reached over and wrapped her arms around me. She whispered with great effort as she struggled to tell me, "thank you for letting me be in my own home and surrounded with all of this love." We were Mom's hip one last time.

HOME HELPERS
SAN RAMON AND DANVILLE CALIFORNIA
231 Market Place, Ste 21
San Ramon, CA 94583
PHONE: 925.236.2477
TOLL FREE: 1.888.99-HELPER
EMAIL: *robertJo@HomeHelpers.cc*

The Capacity to Love Our Clients

by ROBERT JO, CSA

HELLO, MY NAME IS ROBERT JO. AFTER SPENDING MORE THAN 10 YEARS IN THE Tri-Valley area in California, I began to see how many families could appreciate a helpful hand. I opened the local Home Helpers office in August 2005, providing Senior Care, New Moms and Working Parents, Recuperative Care and/or Continuing Care services to our community.

With a background in management and as a Certified Senior Advisor (CSA), rest assured you and your loved ones will receive excellent care and companionship with Home Helpers. I believe in caring for clients as if I were caring for members of my own family. My caregivers are carefully chosen to meet the specific needs of my clients.

Not only am I passionate about serving clients, but I am also passionate about serving my community. As a respected member of the Tri-Valley Chinese Bible Church, I truly enjoy working with people.

Here's a story from one of our clients:

I WAS VERY TENSE WHEN STARTED LOOKING FOR A CAREGIVER FOR MY HUSBAND. He was recently out of the hospital after fighting off pneumonia and he was too exhausted to participate much in the search. With diagnosis of C.O.P.D. he was on oxygen 24/7 and his memory loss problem meant he didn't remember care protocols. Suddenly I had his care and all his business affairs added to my daily routines. Everything was new and sometimes I was given poor or contradictory instructions about how to manage his oxygen and other medical devices. I interviewed several agencies briefly by phone and chose four to meet in person. I asked the same questions of each of the four and listened carefully. When Robert Jo of Home Helpers answered, "How do you choose your caregivers?" he answered by saying they wanted to be sure their caregivers actually have the capacity to love their client. I became very alert. That's how we met our caregiver Lee.

Lee talked to David in our home while I asked Robert more questions about Lee's experience and about needing someone with a fairly flexible schedule since I have medical problems of my own requiring a schedule of treatments and exercise. The match felt right immediately and as time goes by we appreciate Lee and Home Helpers more and more. Lee is flexible, always on time, scrupulous about David's need and taught me a few things and when David is confused or forgetful. We take outing with David using his power chair and portable oxygen and lets David know he enjoys it. His sense of humor matched David's very well. He makes sure he understands when new situation arises and he keeps me informed of his observations and takes messages carefully. He has handled lots of impromptu situations like the time the oxygen concentrator failed to work and the many times David has been overwhelmed by managing daily tasks like making lists or using the computer or receiving delivery or making an appointment. When David asks for Lee's advice Lee has shown excellent skill in communication. And he's so versatile. He even fixed our doorbell (which certainly isn't on his job description.) So when I had to be out of town for 9 days I was not at all worried. Lee adjusted his schedule so that he was present everyday for 12 hours each day—a big commitment. And I knew that Robert would back him up if he needed any help. I came back refreshed. Everything went beautifully. What more can I say? My anxiety level has gone way down. My husband and I can enjoy our times together. We have support.

We've got David on an antibiotic again but we're quite hopeful he'll be able to attend and enjoy our son's wedding on September 6th. I didn't know how to say that the quality and communication between David and I have improved because of all subtle things Lee says and does. He helps me not miss things that might be important. David actually has fun with Lee much of the time. We're very appreciative.

RIGHT AT HOME OF DELAWARE COUNTY, PA
111 Carlton Place • Media, PA 19063
RIGHT AT HOME OF
NEW CASTLE COUNTY, DE
1500 N. French St. • Wilmington, DE 19801
PHONE: 610.566.6650 • EMAIL: *info@rahdelco.com*
In New Castle County, DE: 302.652.1550

Finding the Right Caregiver Through Right At Home

by JOE & ALLISON BAKEY
Owners, Right At Home

This story was written by the client's daughter.

MOST CHILDREN DO NOT PLAN FOR THE DAY WHEN THEY WILL NEED TO GET outside help for a parent. They don't anticipate, or more likely just don't want to think about, their parent not being able to take care of themselves anymore. When it is not possible to take a parent into your home, if you do not live close to your parent(s), if you are still raising a family and working full time, what are you to?

Periodically over the years my mother required assistance at home as a result of hospital and nursing home stays. When you are told that your mother is no longer sick enough to stay in a hospital or nursing home but not well enough to be at home by herself, you find out from the social worker there are outside home health care agencies that can provide help. That is how I found out about the agencies I used for my mother. The last agency was my favorite. When the owner came to the nursing home to access my mother's needs, I knew we had found the right one. Although I was the one dealing with her needs, he directed his attention to my mother and I was touched by the respect he showed her. My mom did not appear to be just another client to him but rather someone he took a real interest in.

Home health care was a challenge because my mother did not want a stranger in her home and that is quite understandable. However she did relent and we did begin the process. I believe the hardest part of the process is finding the right person. However, I was blessed in that the agency had a great staff that understood this and worked most patiently with me. If someone did not work out, another person was sent and the process continued until a good fit was made. No system will ever be 100% without bumps, but once you have a person with your parent that you know has their best interests at heart and truly cares about them, you sleep better, breathe easier, and get through your days much more lighthearted. The benefit of using an agency is that if your assigned worker cannot make it, they can send someone else. If you have a friend or caretaker not associated with an agency helping you with your loved one and they cannot make it for some reason, you are left scrambling.

The main reason my mom needed someone was because she was not eating enough. She was a picky eater and because some of the caregivers she had were from Africa, we had some menu issues but also had some laughs as well at the names my mom assigned some of her new meals. It was a learning experience for all involved but we managed.

My mom did not have any particular health issue that was feared would end her life, her "batteries" just got weaker and weaker over time. As a result she did not go out as much as she once did so home health care provided the much needed social interaction she was missing. Finding a health care aid is a bit like being Goldilocks and trying to find those people that are "just right." Some workers were too quiet, some were too loud, but over time, we found the "just right" ones and they added to my mom's life and became her friends.

As a result of the many conversations I had with the agency staff that are part of the process, I fostered a relationship with the girls, one in particular, and when she and another staff member showed up at my mom's funeral, I was touched beyond belief. To this day it still brings tears to my eyes when I think about it.

Home health care is not an easy decision to make for either the client or the family but finding the right agency and caretakers can help take some of the anxiety out of dealing with an infirmed loved one and provide them with the assistance and care they need.

COMFORT KEEPERS—MISSISSAUGA
Senior Care Provider
107 Dundas Street West
Mississauga, Ontario, L5B 1H8, Canada
PHONE: 905.272.7489
WEBSITE: *www.seniorcaretalk.ca*

First Contact, First Client

by KELLY REVENTAR

IT WAS CLEARLY NOT WHAT I WAS EXPECTING. I PRESSED HIS APARTMENT BUZZER and heard a voice that was full of life and zeal, full of energy and the will to live. You can tell from the tone of his voice that there was that enthusiasm, that excitement to have someone come over. I guess I was expecting someone more downcast…someone less enthusiastic. I pictured in my mind someone who would be bitter about the unfair unravelling of events the past year, the discovery of the big "C." But I guess I was wrong…and that was a good thing.

The doctors said that he had about six months to live. In his early eighties, he looked quite good. Of course, we all know the funny looking side-to-side-gnawing chin motion that our grandparents used to make at that age. The one they normally did when they didn't have their dentures on. But aside from that, he was still independent and lively.

He was an entertainer in his younger years, a singer with a lovely strong baritone. He loved watching both American and Canadian Idol and tells me those guys cannot sing. "I can beat them anytime!" he proudly proclaims. And I actually think he can. He demonstrated his vocal prowess and boy was I impressed. Although in hindsight, I had to admit that I didn't know half of the songs he sang, except for the ever famous "My Way" by Frank Sinatra.

FRIENDS AND FAMILY

It still astounds me how some people can have no one at the end of their lives. Perry, my client, called me "his friend" just after my first visit. I wasn't sure how to take this. I looked at it as somewhat of an honour to be called a "friend" by someone who just met me the first time. Another way of seeing it though was maybe, he didn't have a lot of friends and that it means a lot to him that there is someone who drops by his place once a week just to spend time talking, watching TV, and basically just hanging out.

WHAT WAS AND WHAT IS

"I used to be a wonderful singer! I made so many people happy, you know!" he exclaimed. "But I guess now, with this darn disease, it's all gone…it's all finished", he said. His words kept resounding in my head. "I could have been… I would have been…you fill in the blanks." What once was a life full of endless possibilities, of great dreams to be attained, was now limited to the constraints of the four walls of his apartment.

He still had that wonderful baritone which he would occasionally flaunt. It was actually quite entertaining having someone sing to you. "I left my heart…in San Francisco…high on a hill…it calls to me." He was surprised that I knew who sang that. "Isn't that Tony Bennett?" I asked.

I could just imagine him singing in Vegas, wearing his immaculate white tuxedo, catering to the constant applause of the crowd. "I could have been," he says, "I could have been."

STICK IT UP HIS BUM!

I see him every Saturdays. And this past Saturday was one of self-discovery. I learned that I've started caring about him. It is frightening letting a person into your circle of care…being vulnerable…letting your walls down and opening yourself up to the possibility of getting hurt. And that scared the heck out of me. Seriously!

I knew when I started volunteering that I may face the possibility of getting hurt if I started caring. I didn't know that it'd stare me right in the face this soon though. I guess I was just rationalizing, but grumpiness and complaints aside, he's a sweet, old man who's got a passion for singing and loves watching sports. And okay, though I'd hate to admit it but he's kind of grown on me.

But back to caring. How did I discover my Eureka moment? Well, it's a funny albeit somewhat uncomfortable thing that happened.

"These darn pills!" he exclaimed, "They mask the pain, but make me constipated!" "Oh Crap!" I thought to myself. And yeah, I mean literally. What do I do now? He hadn't taken a dump the past three days. Well, to my relief he apparently complained to his nurse about his "difficulty in going" and she prescribed certain things for him to buy. Which, being the kind, angelic soul that I am volunteered to buy it for him. Yeah right! KY lubricating jelly, a box of suppositories, an enema...well, you get the idea. For those who are new to these things, which I was, they help you get "unplugged" but have to be administered up the bum. And that...ladies and gentlemen...is where all the fun begins. Use your imagination folks! To cut a long story short, I didn't have to do it for him. But I realized that I would have done it for him, if the call of duty required. That was a big revelation for me...that I cared, and was willing to stick these meds up his bum if required. But alas, the opportunity passed me by. And by all means, that was a *huge* sigh of relief!

A SIGN OF THINGS TO COME

"I get these dizzy spells", he tells me. "It's like one second, I'm standing up, then another, I get woozy and can't help myself from falling." That was his reason for the huge cut on his forehead, a big, quarter-sized blotch of dried blood on his pale, balding forehead.

It was a sign of things to come. It was a red flag that things weren't getting any better...that things were beginning to go downhill from there. It was a strange feeling for me, one of apprehension on one hand, and one of expectancy on the other. I was afraid that his health was becoming worse but also knew that this was eventually going to happen.

ALL DOWNHILL FROM THERE

It all started going downhill from there. Ever since Perry complained about his dizzy spells, he started having falls more often. And one day, I got a call from the hospice saying that he's finally agreed to be transferred to a physical hospice, a house that provided hospice care. They asked me if I could swing by his apartment and pack some things for him. I've packed my clothes and belongings several times because of my job but this time, it was different. I was packing for someone's final journey...one that would eventually lead to his death.

JUST LIKE A BABY

He was so happy. I hadn't seen him that content ever since I started my visits with him. "They treat me just like a baby here," he said. "They bathe me, feed me, and change my underpants when I spoil them. And, the people here really like my singing. They applaud me every time I sing. I haven't felt this special for quite some time" he said, referring to his royal treatment at the hospice.

THE DREADED CALL

It was about 12 a.m. when I got the call from the nurse at the hospice. She said that she thinks Perry might be in his last hours. Since he did not have any family around, and he seemed to always talk about me, his good friend, the hospice people thought that I should be there when his time is up. I arrived there after a couple of hours. His breathing was different now and his feet were pretty cold. The nurse said this was pretty normal for a person in his last hours of life. I stayed beside him, spoke to him, held his hand, and said my goodbye. Some people say that hearing is the last thing to go.

THE FINAL CURTAIN

He held on for a couple more hours and finally his spirit gave way. It was all over. He was gone. This was my first time to experience death firsthand. I've lost my friend. There was a feeling of sadness for the loss, but strangely enough, there was also one of gratitude. Gratitude in being able to become part of one's life though short it may be, and see the world from a different perspective and derive the beauty from it no matter what the circumstance.

In his funeral service, I read…

> "It was a pleasure to have gotten to know you Perry. Thank you for allowing me to share a special part of your life. You have allowed me to see life in a different way. That it's not just about the daily grind, but about what effect you have on people's lives. In our brief friendship, you certainly did have a positive effect on me. The people in the hospice certainly loved your beautiful voice. Sing with the angels Perry, and sing to your heart's content."

And this is my story of how I decided to become a Comfort Keeper. How one man changed my perspective of life. My name is Kelly Reventar, and I am a Comfort Keeper.

BERKEN SENIOR CARE, LLC
2300 McDermott, Suite 200-296
Plano, Texas 75025
PHONE: 214.808.2006
EMAIL: *Ken@berkenseniorcare.com*
EMAIL: *Roberta@berkenseniorcare.com*

I Promise

by KEN & ROBERTA LABART

EVERY DAY, MILLIONS OF FAMILIES FIND THEMSELVES FACED WITH THE REALITY of experiencing a serious illness that requires assistance, support and compassion. We pray each day for the blessings we have within each of our own lives. However, a day comes when a serious circumstance hits home, and we are faced with a need. I faced that day recently, when my husband succumbed to a serious illness. I was overwhelmed with emotion, concern, and fear, with a situation that I truly needed help with. I now have become the primary head of the household, with a single income, and the need to work and care for not only my husband, but our two young daughters as well. I was afraid that I would not be able to handle this situation. I was also so afraid that I would not be able to afford the additional expense that this assistance would cost.

I had no idea where to go, who to call, or even where to start. I was given the name of a company right here in my local area, by a member of our church. The company's name was Berken Senior Care. I told her that I didn't have a senior that needed assistance, but instead it was my husband. She said that she understood, but told me to give them a call, you'll be glad you did. "I promise." When I made that call, and after talking with them for just a short period time, I knew I had found my savior. They were caring and compassionate, and they gave me a sense of calm and comfort with their sympathy and experience. They offered to drop by my home, at my convenience, to meet with me and talk about what they could do to assist me with my needs. They offered me more than just their services to assist me, more so they offered me a compassionate and caring friendship. This, combined with their services, provided me a support system beyond any I could have imagined. And the cost was much more reasonable that I had expected. Most companies offer similar services, but not many provide the comfort, care, trust and compassion that Berken Senior Care did, for me.

Berken Senior Care has assisted me with the care of my children, my husband, my pets, and most of all provided me the opportunity to manage my own life, with a little more ease. They help me with getting my daughters ready for school, prepare their breakfasts, and fix their school lunches, and even take them and pick them up from school. When they return home, they assist with their homework, snacks, and even prepare their dinner, if I'm not available to. They provide care, comfort, and assistance for my husband in addition to the household. They transport him to and from doctor's appointments, therapy sessions, and even pick up prescriptions, along with groceries, as we need them. They keep our home neat and clean, and do laundry as needed. They truly are life savers. I'm challenged each day with being the sole head of a household, and all of the needs and responsibilities required to just maintain some sense of normalcy. Without Berken Senior Care, I would still be struggling with the basics. They handle the daily routines of my home, which allows me the quality time to provide the hugs, kisses, and love to my family, that they all truly need and deserve.

I can't say enough about Berken Senior Care. They were here when I need them the most, for all sorts of things. There were so many things that I had no idea that a senior care company would or even could provide. They have truly have become not only my caregivers, but they have become a huge part of my family. I am truly blessed to have them in my life, and I personally thank them each and every day.

COMFORT KEEPERS HOME CARE
2951 S 21st Place
La Crosse, WI 54601
PHONE: 608.784.3357

It's a Better Life for Betty

by MARK STOWERS

THE CHILDREN OF BETTY HAD BUSY LIVES WITH ALL OF THEM WORKING, RUNNING their own households and having kids to mange and take to places, so when Betty became came home after a fall; they had difficulty in helping Betty without burning themselves out in the process.

The family was torn as to what to do; the caregiver they found through an advertising posting in the newspaper was not working out with their mother. She would go out in the garage and smoke several cigarettes and leave their mother alone, she would invite her family over and have them there when she was to take care of their mother, yet the family didn't want to spend the money for an "agency" to come in even though at one point their lawyer suggested it.

With an agency they are more accountable to the family, and have more assets to keep the schedule continuing and provide structure to the caregivers the attorney had said.

Now after many months they saw that it may be worth a try. The live in caregiver was asking for more and more time away and what the family felt they were turning back into taking care of Betty. All the daughters worked and had household they had to manage.

After a couple of month of covering for the caregiver they were spending more time with Betty than their families. They decided to try some local "agencies" and found one that they thought may work.

Comfort Keepers came in and started to help Betty, within the first week the neighbors notice a difference in Betty's appearance and attitude. They thought she looked healthier and stronger when they met her outside enjoying the summer sun.

For their first two week there were several caregivers in there and then one caregiver and Betty clicked and became fast friends. Now Betty and her caregiver are out and about several days a week and the children can now come home and enjoy Betty, not worrying about the household cleaning and maintenance. Thanks to the "agency" and the caregiver, Betty now always has a friend with her.

MARK STOWERS
2951 S 21th Place
La Crosse, WI 54601
PHONE: 608.317.3351
FAX: 608.784.3397
EMAIL: *info@hearmoreaids.com*

Just to Hear My Grandchildren's Voices

by MARK STOWERS

A client told us a story about our impact on her father.

MY DAD USED TO CRY WITH FRUSTRATION BECAUSE HE WAS TRYING TO TALK TO his grandchildren and couldn't understand them because of his bad hearing. He said "love you" and just hung up the phone. I had had seen him try to have conversation several times before but just couldn't hear to what they were telling him. Even thought he had a hearing aid it was still difficult for him to hear on the phone, some screeched when he put it up to his ear with the hearing aid in, other were just not loud enough to hear.

One day a lady from Hear More Aids came to the independent living home were my dad was living and showed the resident the newest technology of amplified phones for the hearing impaired. My dad told me about it the next time I visited and I looked at the information, he wanted me to look at, something he had started doing since he went to independent living. I checked on the web site hearmoreaids.com and saw that these items just might help him hear his grandchildren, so we bought him a new phone that had a volume control on it so he could turn it up.

When we got it we plugged it in, we called my daughter and had him talk to her, he could hear her and was very happy that he could now talk to and listen to his favorite people in the whole world. Find hearing devices for the hearing impaired in your life by visiting *www.HearMoreAides.com.*

A Love Story

by MARLA BECK
Owner, Andelcare

MR. AND MRS. KING WERE LIVING A QUIET LIFE TOGETHER FOR YEARS. MR. King was an artist and his wife was his muse. Mr. King loved his wife more than anything and would do anything for her. There was tangible evidence of this love on the walls of their home. Paintings of a beautiful brunette with soulful eyes would gaze upon you in every room. They had no family left and no real friends they could turn to since they were both in their 80's and their friends had passed on in recent years along with their children. Mrs. King was diagnosed with Alzheimer's and Mr. King took on the job of caring for her day-in and day-out on his own for years. As often happens, Mr. King did not want to admit that his wife was failing before his eyes so he convinced himself that she really wasn't too bad. He took on the job of caring for two people with no support. One day it just became too much, he was exhausted, they were both malnourished, the house was unkempt and Mrs. King became delusional because of a urinary tract infection.

By the time Andelcare became involved with this couple, Mrs. King was in late stage Alzheimer's and was being discharged by the hospital. Mr. King had finally admitted to himself he needed help but he refused to have his wife moved to a home. He first had us come in for 12 hour shifts to care for her, and to help Mr. King navigate through daily life. The nights were still his time to care for his wife. He wanted that time desperately so he could still feel that he was doing his part and honoring his wedding vows to the love of his life. Life became ever more difficult for both as her illness progressed. It got very difficult for our caregivers to even get her out of bed. Our caregivers would ask her to push down with her arms to help get out of bed and she would do just the opposite. Getting her dressed for the day became especially creative; asking her to put her arm down to get her to put her arm up, etc. One night when they were alone, Mrs. King fell and Mr. King went to help her up and he fell too. At that point neither one could get up so Mr. King crawled to the phone and called 911. The time had come—they needed someone in the home 24 hours per day.

Mrs. King finally went into the hospital for the last time with complications from Alzheimer's. Mr. King had met various caregivers during his wife's in home care, but one particular caregiver struck a chord with both of the Kings. Mrs. King would become calm when she was in the room and Mr. King trusted her completely. He asked, "Could Dorothy now be their only caregiver?" By this time, as sometimes happens, Dorothy cared for both of them like they were her relatives. She took him to the hospital and later to the hospice facility every day to see his wife. She advocated and communicated on his behalf because he was broken hearted knowing his wife was slipping away. Often his tears and sobs were heard only by Dorothy as he tried to prepare himself for the inevitable. She provided meals for him and kept his house in order and listened, listened, listened.

When Mrs. King passed on, Dorothy helped Mr. King find a place to live where he would be cared for. She helped him clean out his home of 40 years of memories, planted flowers and cleaned up the front yard which provided some curb appeal for prospective buyers. Over the course of many months, Dorothy successfully brought a man through his initial grief into the next stage of his life. And then—she let go so that she could move on to the next person who needed a great caregiver and he could move on too.

Many times professionals, children and friends want to help a senior make decisions for themselves or their spouses' care and wonder why their advice is not taken. As is true in this love story, sometimes the senior just wants to do it their own way and we need to learn to let it be.

REVERSE MORTGAGE ORIGINATOR
Atascadero, California
PHONE: 805.441.8916
EMAIL: *hollandcash@aol.com*
California Department of Real Estate Salesperson
Licensee #01795145
Certified National Reverse Mortgage Loan Advisor

What Goes Around

by MARLAN J. HOLLAND

WHEN I FIRST MET HER, SHE DIDN'T LIKE ME. WHY SHOULD SHE? I WAS THERE to take away her last remaining daughter. Her first daughter had gone into the Air Force as a nurse. And there was a son, still in high school. But the middle child was special.

Oh, she was cordial, nice enough while waiting for me to take my new blind date out for coffee, but she really didn't like me.

It cost less than two dollars for a great first date. When we returned and I was invited back into the house, she had gone to bed, so I sat down at the piano and played and sang. I was twenty-two and my date was eighteen, just out of high school and starting college. I was on the football team, and since most football players didn't play and sing, I made my desired impression on her daughter.

Times were tough then. Her husband was an out-of-work carpenter who soon after went to Hollywood to build movie sets. She stayed to support the family with a job as a nurse's aide at 75 cents an hour. Her husband found a lady friend and never returned from Southern California. I married her special daughter and took her away.

All her children raised families of their own. When she left the hospital, she alternated living with her son and our family. Over the years, I think she came to believe I was an okay guy.

In 1993, after an extra successful year in business, we had the cash to build her a house of her own on our property. She was eighty-two years old.

We had a secluded hilltop acreage on the Central California Coast covered with mature oak and toyon trees and a few pines. She enjoyed being next door to her daughter. She enjoyed taking care of her cat and watching the deer. She seemed very content. Then, as the years went by, she became a little forgetful. Sometimes she forgot to turn off the burner under her oatmeal. But she never failed to thank me for raking the pine needles and mowing the lawn.

On December 22, 2003, a 6.5 magnitude earthquake centered off the coast at San Simeon trashed our home. “Gram,” as the kids had come to call her, was in town at elder day-care. Luckily, no one was home when the quake hit. There was serious structural damage to the main house but, except for food and broken glass on almost every square foot of the floor, Gram’s house was spared.

After a major clean-up mission by an army of friends and relatives, we moved into Gram’s little house. She made us feel very welcome. She said she enjoyed the company. Actually, she wasn’t feeling very well. She had difficulty breathing enough oxygen. The doctor said there was a problem with her lungs. We decided it might have been the result of something she breathed during the war when she worked as a welder in the shipyards. But she did not have to go to the hospital. She was able to stay at home.

On Valentine’s Day, she passed away peacefully in her own bed, in her own little house, surrounded by her own family.

As is true for most of us, the equity in our property accounted for most of our estate. Our home was not insured against earthquake damage and it cost almost $200,000.00 to rebuild. As if that wasn’t enough bad news, the real estate bubble evaporated just as we were ready to sell our property and move to a smaller place. Most of our nest egg evaporated with it.

So where’s the happy ending? What came around?

Well, soon after the earthquake, my wife’s brother began construction of a guesthouse on his property. On July 7th, 2007 (7/7/07), we moved into our new home. We now have an unwritten life-time lease on a beautiful little house on “La Familia Place.” And, from my home office, I am now originating Reverse Mortgages for seniors on the Central California Coast.

ELIZA ONE, INC.
Holistic Care Coordination
and End of Life Navigation
5871 Cedar Lake Road, Suite 216
Minneapolis, MN 55416
PHONE: 612.202.5728
WEBSITE: *www.elizaoneinc.com*

Learning to Listen from the Heart

by MARY CHAPA, RN
President

In honor of Corporal David Nunez Chapa, US Army, WWII 1941–1945
November 2, 1916 – September 16, 2008

BORN IN SANDIA, TEXAS NOVEMBER 2, 1916, CORPORAL DAVID NUNEZ CHAPA, 200th Coast Artillery 1st Battalion A Battery was a patriot who was proud to serve his country. He had a big heart and a generous spirit. He served with others from the New Mexico area and was shipped to the Philippine Islands and Clark Air Force base on September 8, 1941. Clark Air Force Base was attacked the day after Pearl Harbor and David's unit was responsible for covering the retreat of the Northern Luzon Force into Bataan. As the war situation began to deteriorate David's regiment was surrendered to the Japanese Army where he survived the atrocities of the 65-mile "Bataan Death March" only to be held prisoner for over 3 years and 8 months. David was never bitter but believed he survived because he was "a good work horse," he said the Japanese kept him alive so he could work and he learned about hard work from his father while growing up on a farm in Texas. After the war and his rescue from the concentration camp David went home to Texas but later decided to start a new life and moved to St. Paul, Minnesota where he found work, met and married his wife Mary and raised his 5 children and 5 grandchildren.

As I reflect on my father David's changing medical needs over the last few years of his life I realized how well he did with balancing his independence and his limitations due to chronic and complex health conditions. I learned many life lessons from Dad but I especially remember the importance of "listening" to the client, I hear his voice in my ear every time I want to make decisions and assumptions based on my own knowledge and experiences. My father was right about 98% of the time, he knew his body and how it responded or not to various medications or treatments and he had to remind me and his physician that sometimes what we thought would work, did not work for him. He was a good sport though, he would try things for us only to prove to us he was right and not suffering from any forms of dementia, the joke was usually on us. I realize how important the many gifts my father left behind would be for me personally and how they make a difference in the live of my client's.

After my father died last fall I thought about how much I used my nursing skills to manage his medical care over several years, I did the same when my mother was dying from cancer and subsequently other friends and family members would request my help. When my sister died this spring unexpectedly I organized the work that needed to be done, coordinating with family and friends to close out all her personal affairs. Having navigated through end of life activities for my father, mother and a younger sister I learned through very different experiences and it became clear that being a daughter, sister and friend with a health, healing and end of life background could be helpful to others. Perhaps this is the real gift my father left me, the gift of care and concern for others who may not have family readily available to help them during difficult times. Some choices are obvious and other decisions come to us unlooked for but life is an interesting journey and I consider myself a strong independent woman; a survivor and leader with gifts to share, I learned from my Dad.

David Nunez Chapa died suddenly on September 16, 2008 at the Veterans Hospital in Minneapolis but his sense of humor, love of family and generous spirit will live on as I demonstrate the life lessons of listening with my heart.

Rest in Peace Dad, your memory lives on in the lives I touch every day.

PATRICK RODEN RN PhD
Website: *www.AgingInPlace.com*

Mavis Lindgren: Grandma Wears Running Shoes

by PATRICK RODEN, RN, PhD

A critical care nurse, Patrick Roden, was a medical volunteer at the Portland Marathon of 1992 when he came to the aid of the celebrated 85-year-old marathoner, Mavis Lindgren. They became fast friends and he has escorted her for other marathons until her last at age 90. "Mavis changed the way I viewed aging," Patrick said, "The medical model tends to focus on what goes wrong in aging—and neglects to inform us about what goes right. She inspired me to begin working on a Ph.D. in aging and human development." Here is their story:

Night's chill lingered in the air and the silence was broken by the sounds of songbirds. The sun was just beginning to rise on a crisp October morning in 1992. Suddenly the squeaking brakes of a rental truck and the clanging of folding chairs shattered the serenity. With military precision, the volunteers began to set up the first aid station at the 18-mile marker. I was one of those volunteers and this was the annual running of the Portland Marathon.

It took an hour to set up and go through my checklist. The first aid kit was in order and the communications were working. We were ready. Soon the elite runners would be flying through, followed by a seemingly endless sea of participants. The conditions were perfect: a bright clear indigo sky, golden fall leaves. All of us were anticipating an inspiring day.

The morning had been uneventful at our station. The usual blisters, Vaseline applied to chaffed skin, hydration to the dehydrated, and lots of moral support. One pregnant woman reached the 18-mile point and could go no further so we loaded her in the ambulance. They taxied her to the finish line and her anxiously awaiting husband.

It was now late afternoon and the sea of runners had dwindled to a trickle of determined souls. The frequent and now familiar static that preceded a message from the EMS broke the airwaves. An elderly woman was reported down near the 18-mile mark, in our territory. I waited for a person fitting the description to pass, and no one did. Strapping on my first aid kit, I set out to investigate.

Running upstream, I began to think, how elderly could they mean? Whoever it was, he or she had gone 18 miles, and this was a marathon after all…50, maybe 60, I thought. As I rounded the bend I saw a young woman attending the injured runner who looked like Mother Theresa in running shorts! The young woman explained that another runner had cut in front of the injured woman and knocked her down as she stepped towards the curb. As I listened, I assessed the situation. The injuries included an obviously fractured wrist as well as a small bump on the head. "Her name is Mavis," the young woman said.

"Mavis, I would like to escort you to the first aid station," I began… "Young man, I'm going to finish this race," she politely interrupted. After a few seconds of negotiating, I held up her injured arm and we briskly took off for the station (or so I thought).

Amazed, I blurted out "How old are you?" "I'm 85." She pointed to her number pinned to the front of her T-shirt. "Every year, they give me the number of my age. This year I'm number 85. " What do you mean each year?" I asked.

Mavis Lindgren had run all over the world. She had appeared many times on TV, radio, and magazines such as Runner's World, Sports Illustrated, and The New York Times, and been mentioned in books such as Age Wave (Ken Dychtwald) and Grandma Wears Running Shoes (Patricia Horning Benton). She was no stranger to Portland, either. All along the course there were signs encouraging her and the cheers followed her every step! Two middle-aged women ran up and hugged her exclaiming that they wanted to be just like her when they grew up.

Mavis and I reached the finish line arm-in-arm, right into interviews for the 6'oclock news (I have the video). I was asked to escort her for the entire race the next year in 1993, and it became a tradition.

She retired from running at age 90 after the 1997 marathon. It was her 75th and final 26.2-mile outing. Phil Knight of Nike, had a custom pair of "Air Mavis" running shoes made especially for her final marathon. Her two daughters and grandchildren accompanied us and it was an emotional finale to an illustrious running career.

What makes her story all the more exceptional to me is that at age 62, Mavis was leading a sedentary life, spending most of time reading, writing and knitting. She had suffered four bouts of pneumonia in five years and, as a retired nurse, she knew the antibiotics weren't the long-term solution. Something had to change. A doctor urged her to join an early bird walking group. At age 70, encouraged by her son, she ran her first marathon! Two years later, she established a record of 4:33.05, and for the next eight years, held world's best time for women 70 and over. And at 84 she finished the Los Angeles marathon in 6 hours 45 minutes-the fastest woman in her age category. "After I started running, I never had another cold," she said.

Asked what his message was, Ghandi replied: "My life is my message." This could well be said about Mavis Lindgren.

OAK MEADOWS
Director of Community Relations
8131 Fourth St N
Oakdale, MN 55128
PHONE: 651.578.0676
WEBSITE: *www.oak-meadows.org*
EMAIL: *kim@aok-meadows.org*

Connecting With Others Enriches Seniors' Lives

by STEPHANIE WEIGER
Former staff person and current volunteer at Oak Meadows with contributing ideas from Kim Prayfrock

HAVING DECIDED TO MOVE TO INDEPENDENT SENIOR LIVING, MANDY DIAmond's unexpected health concern changed her plans. In 2003, Mandy moved into Oak Meadows Assisted Living and has bloomed where she landed. Mandy has taken advantage of the ala carte health services, the daily meals and the transportation services to reserve her energies for the life enriching activities that have made her apartment her home.

Mandy and her husband raised their four boys in a neighborhood not far from where Oak Meadows is built. She enjoyed her children, neighbors and the opportunities that came along with living in an area filled with young families. Long before there were organized mom groups, Mandy socialized with and supported other moms throughout the neighborhood and especially as a member of her sons' elementary school mom's choir. Years later after having been at Oak Meadows for awhile, Mandy and another choir mom found each other and renewed their friendship. When their story became known, these two friends were featured in the local paper that had heard of their reconnecting after so many years.

Age is not a factor for friendship and Mandy has also made many connections with people younger than she is. The local MOMS Club visits Oak Meadows each month and Mandy is often the first senior to arrive for the scheduled activity. MOMS Club members are mothers of children kindergarten age or younger who live within a few miles of Oak Meadows. Mandy waits anxiously to see the girls and boys who have grown so much since their last visit and to catch up on the children's activities and the young mother's challenges. Because many of the MOMS Club members do not have an older generation of family living nearby, Mandy and the other seniors at Oak Meadows have provided much-needed advice, direction and hope to the sometimes frustrated and weary young mothers.

In addition to bonding with friends old and new, Mandy rolled up her sleeves at Oak Meadows and dug into the gardening activities, card-making, cooking, dominoes, volunteering as an envelope stuffer at a local church, tea parties, holiday decorating, church services and Wii bowling. Last year, Mandy's Wii bowling team was challenged by another senior living community. After learning of the challenge, the team secured a sponsor, got matching T-shirts and won the competition!

Mandy has also been busy entering her handmade items into the county fair. In the last three years, Mandy has won two 2nd place ribbons, one 3rd place ribbon, two 4th place ribbons and one 5th place ribbon for her crocheted baby blankets, hats, booties, and bibs. When she isn't crocheting baby items, Mandy makes and sends crocheted cloth bandages to overseas hospitals.

At Oak Meadows, The 90+ Club is a very exclusive group and membership depends on having reached at least 90 years of age. Mandy is a member of the 90+ Club. There are over 30 members in The 90+ Club and the monthly meetings provide a chance to socialize and reminisce about life and how it's changed over 90+ years.

While it is relatively easy to see how active and engaged in life Mandy Diamond is at Oak Meadows and in the surrounding community, what is more difficult to express is the care with which she goes about these activities and the care she shows everyone she encounters on daily basis. Her enthusiasm for everything that life has to offer is truly contagious and she's doing her best to make sure others have a chance to catch it.

ANGELICARE IN-HOME COMPANION CARE
2190 N. Winery Ave., Suite #102
Fresno, CA 93703
PHONE: 559.453.0151
WEBSITE: *www.angelicare4seniors.com*

Caring for Aunt Florence

by TERRY GARCIA

LIKE MANY OTHERS, MY LIFE CHANGED AFTER PROVIDING CARE FOR A LOVED one. For me, it was helping my mother care for my father, who battled cancer, strokes and other ailments at the end of his life. I also experienced the negative side of caregiving, when we faced manipulation and theft issues with an independent caregiver that was caring for my grandmother in another state. Both of these events impacted my life and led to the decision of dedicating myself to improving the lives of seniors.

Those who love helping seniors understand that providing care isn't just a job or a responsibility. It's an opportunity to not only make a difference in their clients lives, but your own life as well. For many of us, Aunt Florence was one of those who enriched our lives as much or more than we contributed to hers.

Aunt Florence was getting ready to turn 95 and was planning a trip to celebrate her birthday with her extended family, Bob and Tina and their brood of kids and grandkids. Florence loved to travel and during her lifetime she had traveled the world, including attending 3 Olympics Games. She was independent, full of life and very opinionated. She read several papers daily, didn't own a TV and lived by herself on a 5 acre farm where she raised goats.

In preparation for the upcoming trip, Bob and Tina visited Aunt Florence at her farm in Northern CA., to insure she was ready for the trip. After Bob and Tina had gotten back home in Fresno, they called Aunt Florence to let her know they got home alright, there was no answer. After a day of unanswered calls, they called one of her nearby friends to check on her. She found Florence on the floor, who she had laid for two days. Dehydrated and weakened, she had to be hospitalized.

After she was released from the hospital, Bob brought Aunt Florence home to stay with them until she recuperated. Bob and Tina knew that Aunt Florence's care would require a lot of attention so they interviewed home care agencies, AngeliCare being one of them. We first started caring for Aunt Florence on a limited basis, but soon it grew into 24/7 care.

Aunt Florence was one of our first clients, so I provided care as well. There were so many things about Aunt Florence that touched all of us. The first thing that everyone recalls was the beautiful smile on her face every time you entered the room. Her smile literally lit up the room and her eyes would twinkle, honestly twinkle, when her eyes met yours. You knew she was glad to see you and regardless of your own mood at the time, Aunt Florence's smile and welcome always made your day better.

It's funny the little things you remember. Florence's allergies always caused her nose to run and I can still hear her say "Blow my nose!" Putting it on paper just doesn't do it justice, you had to hear her say it. Courtney, another caregiver, remembers that Aunt Florence always made her feel "warm and fuzzy," and she recalls always talking to Florence about "that black cat in the room." There was no black cat, but that didn't matter.

Aunt Florence had dementia and as it progressed, she would go back in time and reminisce about past adventures. she would talk to you like you were the person she was with, or she would include you in her journey. Florence liked to travel by train when she was younger and I got to travel with her. She even introduced me to her mother and brother on one of those journeys. Her memories were always happy, and I feel so blessed to have accompanied Aunt Florence to all those places from her room, at the end of the house.

I started my agency from the care experiences I had with my father and grandmother. Unfortunately, my mom left me so suddenly, I never got the chance to do the same for her. Caring for Aunt Florence allowed me the opportunity to feel the intimacy of caring for my own mother. I miss them both.

From Tragedy to Triumph

by ROSALENN & JAY KENNEY

ONE WINTER DAY, ON THE NORTH SHORE OF BOSTON, THERE WAS A TERRIBLE tragedy. An elderly couple in their 90's and both suffering from Alzheimer's disease- still living together in their own home, became victims of an accident. The furnace in their home broke and the indoor temperature started to drop. Because of their condition, neither could communicate effectively nor really understand the potential risk involved with the increasing cold. There was no family living close to check in on them. Many times in New England, neighbors don't see each other for days in the winter, because people stay indoors during the long season. Unfortunately, for this New England couple, Alzheimer's disease put them in a fatal situation.

Eventually, a neighbor went to check in on them because their mail was piling up outside. The woman died of exposure in her nightgown and the husband (Mr. L) was very near death.

Mr. L was a very proud man and worked in the airline industry his whole life. He provided a good life for his wife and daughter. This accident and the loss of his wife were devastating to Mr. L. He was taken to the hospital and then to rehabilitation. Various state agencies and the newspapers became involved in following this case. It was assumed that Mr. L would go into a long term care facility; however he wanted to go home.

Right at Home, In Home Care and Assistance was called in to meet with his family and the healthcare professionals to talk about how Mr. L could go home. He would need to have around-the-clock care with skilled caregivers. Right at Home worked with him and his family to prepare the house for his homecoming (it was in disrepair before the accident), arranged with professionals to have things repaired or replaced and started to pull together a team of caregivers to stay with Mr. L. He had some resources so it was thought that he could be at home for a year or more with that level of care.

Mr. L's team of caregivers was male and female. They loved working with him and created great relationships to support him in his efforts to stay home independently. Right at Home caregivers cooked his meals, reminded him of his medications, helped with his personal care, performed housework, helped him with his personal grooming and showering, transported him to doctor's appointments, and did errands.

Over time, Mr. L was running out of financial resources to pay for his home care. His daughter, who lived in another state, his lawyer and his attorney took him to assisted livings and long term care facilities, so that Mr. L felt like he had a choice in his next steps. In the end, they all came up with a plan to finance his next steps. Mr. L and his daughter began to work with a reverse mortgage broker to discuss financing his care with equity from his house. With the safer reverse mortgage practices and with Mr. L's deep desire to stay at home until he passed away, it was decided to reverse mortgage his home to allow him to stay there as long as possible. The reverse mortgage would allow him to stay home for another two years with 24 hour care and pay his living expenses.

Mr. L did live at home for almost another year. In total, he was able to enjoy almost three years of his life in the home where that terrible accident occurred. He was a proud man, and nothing made him prouder than being self sufficient. His daughter was very grateful to Right at Home because her father was able to live how he wanted to live. She no longer had to worry about his condition and if he was alone. He knew that the Right at Home management and caregiver staff were there making sure that he was safe, secure and well taken care of until the end of his life.

A Tale of Two Sisters

by DAVID A. TRAVLAND, PHD & RHONDA TRAVLAND

WORKING WITH FAMILY CAREGIVERS, THE MOMENTS WE TREASURE MOST ARE the ones that make a lasting impression on our personal views regarding the value of family support. Sally, 89, and Maggie, 85, were sisters and best friends. To understand our experiences with these remarkable ladies, we must share a little of their history.

Each lady had married only once, but Sally's husband, Charlie, had died suddenly forty years earlier. Maggie was still married to her first and only husband, but he was developing symptoms of dementia. Maggie adored her big sister and depended on Sally for emotional support. She always had needed her and now facing a health care crisis, Maggie needed Sally more than ever. With grown children, Maggie still found that her greatest support was her sister.

Sally had been an independent entrepreneur long before women did that sort of thing. Charlie shared her passions and they shared an unconventional life. Maggie saw strength in that, perhaps, even envied it, but she chose the tradition life course for women coming of age in the 1930's. Maggie and Sally loved their husbands very much, but ironically, both men were alcoholics. In that pain, the sisters drew comfort and solace in each other through the years. However, what made Sally stronger made Maggie weaker.

Sally's caregiving to an alcoholic made her tough, independent and determined to succeed in life regardless of the obstacles. She taught her two daughters the resilience a woman must possess to survive life without reliance on a man. Maggie's caregiving, under similar circumstances, made her an enabler. To keep peace, Maggie would buy the alcohol of choice and make sure the stock was in the house—Sally poured every drop she found, hidden around the house, down the drain. Maggie's children grew to tolerate poor treatment by others and her only daughter, Jane, married an alcoholic. Set in motion by Maggie, Jane refused to give up on her own marriage well into her sixties, but that is another story.

Now, with Maggie in trouble due to her husband's health decline, Sally was again becoming a full-time caregiver to Maggie's emotional stability. Sally had been considering selling her home, but did not want to leave her comfortable life without a reason. She needed motivation to give up on the responsibilities of home ownership other than her own limitations. Sally had only recently retired and was getting bored. So, these ladies devised a plan—before they consulted us—to move into an assisted living facility (ALF) together.

Fantasizing that it would be just like when they were children, Maggie and her husband sold their home and moved into the ALF. Sally kept her home, still tentative about losing what remained of her independence, yet she moved into the ALF across the hall from Maggie.

Sally was quick to tell us upon our initial meeting, that her move was voluntary, that she did not need assistance and it was all for Maggie's well-being. Sally thought, at the time, it was the best decision for everyone and would be a test to see if Sally wanted to sell her home. However, Sally was now regretful of her decision. Although she still owned her home, Sally felt stuck because Maggie's husband died during the year they had been in the ALF. Believing Maggie to be helpless because of their history, Sally could not allow herself to consider her own emotional well-being because her sister needed her.

We checked on Maggie, indeed, she was truly adjusting to the ALF. The move and the odd relief provided from her husband's death after years of tending to his needs allowed Maggie to explore independence for the first time in her adult life, even in her mid-eighties. The table had turned and Sally was the one in need. Sally's budding despair seemed rooted in Maggie's new happiness. We turned our full attention to Sally.

Understanding that Sally's initial rationale for moving into the ALF—to care for her sister—was now gone because of Maggie's newfound liberation and excitement about life. Working with Sally, she began to comprehend that she, too, had been a sort of enabler all her life. When Maggie was in need Sally flew to her rescue. She experienced emotional satisfaction when she helped Maggie. Without a husband and her daughters grown, Sally had turned her caregiving devotion completely to her younger and perceived weaker sister. Because of the changes in Maggie, Sally didn't feel very useful anymore.

We helped Sally look at her alternatives, and we hit upon one that really seemed to rekindle her fire. She still owned her large home and it was sitting vacant. They lived in a community without residential rehabilitation facilities for disabled children. There had been several articles in the local paper about the community need. Sally had financial resources and political contacts, and created such a facility using her home.

The activity energized Sally through her own civic engagement and purposeful use of her time. Rather quickly, Sally developed an appreciation for the security she felt living in the ALF instead of feeling resentful. She began to enjoy living across the hall from Maggie while keeping her positive self-identity. By using Sally's strengths and creating a pro-active and positive channel for her, the two sisters are enjoying a happy, healthy friendship. Who could ask for a better outcome?

The Widowed Mother and Her Son: Who is Caring for Whom?

by PATRICK RODEN, RN PHD

OUR CAREGIVER CONSULTING SERVICES BEGAN BECAUSE WE WERE HEALTH CARE professionals, but we barely survived when the role of caregiver turned personal. Through our experiences, we realized that caregivers do not acknowledge they are caregivers for a very long time. We do what we must because of love. No two people exemplify this better than a woman named Cora and her son, Roland. Cora did not define herself as a caregiver; she was a wife and mother. She had managed a farm, as a widow, for many years with Roland's help.

Sadly, Cora had been diagnosed with an aggressive form of cancer two years earlier and the information we received implied that Roland was unable to care for himself. While not physically impaired, Roland was what in the past would have been "slow." Supposedly, Roland would not speak on the phone, refused to write checks, and needed Cora to work out the arrangements for his work. Cora was nearing seventy and her husband, Joe, died nearly a decade earlier. Her only daughter, Crystal, was lost to cancer many years earlier. Basically, Cora did everything, with a few exceptions. So focused was she on her many roles that no plans had been considered for Roland should she die.

Upon meeting Cora, she said she never complained about her numerous duties and that she had grown unaware of Roland's limitations because he was her son. Oh, she said she knew he was not the typical boy, but he was strong, devote to his family and she thought him to just be shy. Besides, she said, she was his mother; who would not be proud of a child who cared for his aging, ill mother? In this statement, we realized we were actually working with two caregivers, each unable to define their role, working without direction and focused on duty and love for each other.

Cora was talkative when we initially met her and our hunch was that nobody else had been available to listen. Exhausting her detailed stories, we finally broached the realities of caregiving that she and Roland must have been experiencing without emotional support. Cora's tales had been eloquent, though not resentful, about Roland's limitations. She had described her own cancer treatments and the impact they had on her stamina, never realizing that Roland had naturally adapted to her needs—especially on the days of chemotherapy.

We asked if she had a plan for Roland if she were absent. Our question took her off guard. She said she never even wondered about it because when she was shopping, running errands, or at the doctor, Roland stuck close to home. He seemed to be fine when she returned. She now had to admit that she was never gone long enough so Roland would have to prepare a meal, wash his own clothes, pay bills, nor had she ever been gone overnight. After many visits with Cora and Roland, Cora conceded that her cancer could be fatal, and agreed to discuss the concrete options "for Roland."

Cora agreed that Roland could not live on the farm by himself, that he needed support and supervision. As we assisted Cora in developing a plan for Roland, her immediate suggestions were that some of her friendly neighbors could look in on Roland to make sure he was OK. This is often the situation with people who are caring for an adult child. The "friendly neighbors" are not likely to accept permanent responsibility for the well-being of a grown man.

We introduced Cora to the idea of an assisted living facility, carefully distinguishing it from a nursing home. In her mind, these places were dark institutions that limited freedoms and the thought terrified her. She questioned who would run the farm? How would this be paid? What about spending money for Roland? How could Roland pay for assisted living? How could he move after she died; he would be scared of the change during his grief? Now, she even wondered if he even understood how sick she really was going to get.

We worked with Cora and Roland to develop a plan of action. This plan included a consultation with an elder law attorney, a tour of local assisted living facilities, selling their property, and other necessities. To Cora's dismay, but absolute delight, Roland was excited about the idea of living 'on his own' in an assisted living facility and encouraged his mother to move with him. See, Roland naturally understood he was his mother's caregiver now even though Cora had not realized it. The rest of the family was gone and he knew his mother actually need him more that he needed her for care. Over the years, it was a sacrifice that he gladly did because Cora had always protected him and her heart had broken when she buried his father and his sister.

Our role, as consultants, bridged the gap between their unspoken fears and active resolutions. The caregiving dualities in their home kept them from talking about aging and illness. Over the next three months, we watched a new relationship emerge between a grown man finding his independence and his loving mother preparing to die. They had time to explore a new, more fulfilling relationship before she died.

BILL RANIERI
321 Hibiscus Trail
Melbourne Beach, FL 32951
PHONE: 321.626.9031

Sports and Son Saved Dad

by BILL RANIERI

I NEVER WOULD HAVE GUESSED ON THAT WARM SUNNY DAY THAT MY DAD would some twenty five years later be diagnosed with Alzheimer's Disease.

He was teaching me how to play tennis. When I hit the ball to him it sometimes took on a life of its own and went twenty feet away from where I aimed it.

"Would you hit the ball to me!" He yelled with growing impatience.

"Dad, I'm trying." I'd yell back with equal impatience.

Dad was a fitness enthusiast. He was always exercising or working. He'd sit down and watch the Yankees or the Giants but he was always up for a tennis match or a game of basketball. He wanted us children to be fitness nuts too. I lovingly fell for his lure.

I remember one time when I wanted to get a job so I might have a buck or two if my girlfriend wanted to go out for a night. Dad asked me if I enjoyed my sports.

"Of course I do, Dad. You know that. I just want to have a few bucks in case Mary wants to go out."

"That's OK, Bill, if you need some money, I'll give you some."

Dad was great. He believed sports built character. What I learned instead that it was dad who was the character.

"Dad, I'm taking Mary out tonight. Can I have twenty dollars?"

"Bill, I have eleven children. Where am I going to get twenty dollars?!!?"

At 84, Dad was diagnosed with Alzheimer's disease. That was three years ago. Meanwhile, Mom has been diagnosed with macular degeneration and glaucoma. There's nothing that gives her more enjoyment than reading.

What are we supposed to do?

Think. Think.

My brother Philip just accepted a job as a high school teacher in New York. His wife was home with their third child. Money was getting tight and Philip knew he would have to get his Master's degree if he was to compete in the school system with any real success.

After we called a family meeting, we popped the question, "Philip, would you and your family move in with Mom and Dad and keep an eye on them while you get your degree? Speaking for his wife,

"Of course, I would love to help out and in the meanwhile, I get free rent."

Three years later Mom is still able to read, but a little less. Dad forgets his grandchildrens' names but he has over fifty of them. Philip has his Master's degree in Education.

Exercise, proper nutrition, a great attitude and some unselfish cooperation on a caregiver's part all combine for an effective prescription for successfully aging in place. Why dad even gets out to play a game or two of doubles (and I always try to hit to him).

VISITING ANGELS
Senior Home Care Agency
5871 Cedar Lake Rd., Suite 101
St. Louis Park, MN 55416
PHONE: 952.544.6300
WEBSITE: *www.angelcaremn.com*

It's All About the Cookies

by RON HAGBERG, CSA & SUSAN GREEN, RN, CSA

HARRIET LIVED ALONE IN A LOVELY CONDOMINIUM IN A TWIN CITIES SUBURB. Her husband, Jim, had passed away shortly after they had moved in, and living with the grief of his loss took quite an emotional toll on her. They had been high school sweethearts and had raised four wonderful children during their 63 years of marriage. Two lived out of state and two daughters, Jeanine and Kris, lived nearby and visited her often.

In the year following Jim's death, Harriet allowed herself to become more and more isolated, not wishing to visit friends as often, less interested in activities she had enjoyed for many years, such as cooking, baking, and knitting. And, she had stopped attending her church regularly.

She had always been a social person who loved to entertain and attend concerts and plays. Her children remembered that their Mother often played the piano, loved to sing, hosted her bridge club every week, and was often complimented on her skills in the kitchen. But, over time, it was evident to Jeanine and Kris that their Mom was slipping.

Although Harriet was doing fairly well physically, her mild dementia made it more and more difficult for her to take care of some of the things that needed to be done around the house. She gave up cooking, baking, and knitting—things she had loved to do—because she had trouble remembering the sequences those activities required. Because Jeanine and Kris both had families and full-time jobs, the time they could help Harriet with housework and shopping was limited. Eventually, they decided Mom needed more help than they could give.

They found a local agency and were generally satisfied with the service—the laundry was getting done, the linens were changed regularly, and Harriet was usually taking her medications on time. But, over time, they became increasingly concerned about the parade of different caregivers in and out and the lack of "spark" and vitality that their Mom had been known for.

Eventually, wanting more for her, they asked if she would mind if they contacted Visiting Angels, referred to them by a family friend. She agreed, and was soon matched with her own Angel, Meghan.

One day, Kris made a point of stopping by at a time when she knew Meghan would be there. As she walked down the hall and approached the condo door, she smelled the fresh aroma of baked goods.

She opened the door quietly, without letting them know she was there, and peeked around the corner to see her Mother and Meghan in the kitchen. They both wore aprons, and were placing hot chocolate chip cookies on the counter to cool. And, they were softly singing Harriet's favorite hymn, "Amazing Grace." When they finished, they were both smiling as Meghan helped Harriet out of her apron. Then, they gave each other a sincere and warm hug.

At that moment, Kris' eyes became moist, and she burst into joyful tears. She realized what the difference was between Meghan and the other caregivers. Without even thinking, she said out loud, "it's all about the cookies!"

The "cookies" are the difference between a caregiver who just does his or her "job," and one who goes out of their way to capture a special moment, or recreate a cherished memory. The "cookies" brought Harriet back to the Mom Jeanine and Kris remembered.

As a wise person said, "People may not remember what you said to them. They may not remember what you did for them. But, they will always remember the way you made them feel."

Make some "cookies" with your loved one today.

NON MEDICAL IN-HOME CARE
4446-1 Dennie Street
Hanmer, Ontario P3P 1S1
705.969.1777
WEBSITE: *www.comfortkeepers.ca*

A Comforting Solution

by SANDRA DESJARDINS
Comfort Keepers

IT WAS A TERRIBLE DAY FOR MR. OGDEN. HE WAS BEING ADMITTED TO A LOCAL nursing home as his three children though it was the best solution for him and for them. Since their mum had died four months ago they felt he had deteriorated significantly and was unable to look after himself. He had also had his license revoked after a very scary accident. While at the nursing home, the staff was very understanding and helpful and prescribed medications to alleviate Mr. Ogden's depression.

After a couple of weeks, Mr. Ogden was feeling much better and begged his children to take him home as he wished to get back to his usual activities and wanted to see his friends. The house had not been put up for sale and the children relented and released him from the facility and brought him home.

While her father was in the nursing home, Suzanne, the oldest daughter, visited our Comfort Keepers to inquire about help for her dad if he decided to come back home. We arranged care and split the 40 hours a week between two of our best caregivers.

Our "Comfort Keepers" stepped up to the task, preparing three meals each day, doing laundry, housekeeping and bathing Mr. Ogden. They also took him out to local parks, visiting his friends, running errands, and will be helping him to enroll in computer classes, in the fall, so he will be able to "surf the net" and keep in touch with his other children, and grand children, who live in British Columbia. The caregivers have been a wonderful support for Mr. Ogden and now have become true companions interacting and sharing the daily chores and meal preparation. The caregivers often help him prepare meals for his entertaining evenings with friends and his children when they are in town.

Mr. Ogden appears to be very happy with the caregivers but has started to repeat himself more frequently and forget where he has put something. Suzanne went with him to the doctor and was dismayed to hear he had early onset dementia. After a discussion with the family, Comfort Keepers extended the hours to 80 per week and continued to stimulate and challenge Mr. Ogden's mind, with card games and simple crosswords. The caregivers were very experienced and would do all the little things to make Mr. Ogden's life more enjoyable. Foot rubs were given to Mr. Ogden every night before each caregiver left. Massages and back rubs were given when Mr. Ogden had his bath. Special home-made goodies were prepared almost every day.

The B.C. children call almost daily to talk to dad and the caregivers and have often told me that the caregivers are like members of their own family. One of the caregivers let me know the other day that she felt that Mr. Ogden's dementia wasn't getting any worse as he seemed quite lucid, humorous and often spoke readily about the day's events.

We are extremely proud of our caregivers and the difference they have made in Mr. Ogden's life. Comfort Keepers Mission is to provide our clients with the highest level of quality of life that is achievable. We shall treat each of our clients with the respect and dignity they deserve, as though we are caring for a member of our own family.

Our "Comfort Keepers" will be there for Mr. Ogden and his children until they no longer need us.

ALICE LORRAINE CARE CENTER
2590 N Monroe St
Monroe MI 48162
PHONE: 734.243.4000
WEBSITE: *www.alicelorraine.com*

Thanksgiving Day 1990

by SUE ANSARI, RN
Founder and Executive Director

THANKSGIVING DAY, 1990—MY 42ND BIRTHDAY. MY GIRLS, LIVELY SIX AND seven-year-olds, were excited to be having their 85-year-old grandmother, my aunt, their half-sister, along with her boyfriend, join us for Thanksgiving Day dinner.

When my grandmother arrived, she asked if I could help my aunt who had been wheelchair-bound for years into the house. As she closed the door behind us, with me standing only inches from her, I faintly heard her whisper, "Oh my, I am so light-headed." Eyelids fluttered and immediately she collapsed, blue and lifeless into my arms. My spunky, independent, beautiful grandmother, as I had known her, was forever gone.

Chaos followed. "Do something!" my aunt screamed at me. I sobbed back that I would not. What seemed like a very long shouting match, probably lasted only seconds as I found myself on the floor compressing the chest of my dear grandmother. A sinking feeling in my own stomach ensued as her brittle ribs and then sternum gave way under my hands. "Call 911!" I shouted. Within minutes the EMT's were beside me. Gram was in ventricular tachycardia—they shocked her many times.

I don't remember much after that, although I know we did not have Thanksgiving Dinner. Mostly, I cried...for days. I cried because she was alive and I was responsible; however, after three days of being intubated, unresponsive and on a respirator, she opened her eyes and pulled her tube.

The days that followed are also a blur. PT evaluation confirmed she would never walk again. The doctor was talking nursing home, so I called one for an appointment and was told they had just opened a new wing—that sounded good to me!

1990, smoking had not yet been banned. The nursing home office was blue with smoke and the administrator's breath smelled like a very dirty ashtray. Not one step further did I care to take, but reluctantly I meandered through dismal, stark accommodations, seeing residents in hallways strapped into their wheelchairs, staring into space. I was shocked to learn that was the new wing!

Needless to say, that was my first and last nursing home visit. My busy life didn't seem conducive to also caring for an invalid grandmother and a wheelchair-bound aunt; however, after that tour, it was a no-brainer—bring Grandma home!

Within days, my grandmother, along with my aunt, plus all other care necessities, were moved into my dining room which overlooked the Detroit River and a huge, unfurling American flag. Her bed I placed directly in front of the window, so every time she opened her eyes, beauty would be seen. Not only had her life changed dramatically, but so had mine. At that moment, the very first "Alice Lorraine Care Center" was born—a Center that I founded two years after my grandmother's death in her hometown of Monroe, Michigan, where she had lived her entire life and where she ultimately died.

During the time I cared for her, I watched with amazement as one who supposedly could never be rehabilitated, within a two-month period was up and walking without even a walker. Her incontinence, which followed the cardiac arrest, within 6 months, was completely reversed. All pills were laxatives, she had no idea how to prepare food, and every freighter that passed by our house was a brand-new exciting experience, which presented itself as a photo opportunity for her. Most of the time, I was totally exhausted, but it was a priceless, unparalleled experience for which I am forever grateful.

While we cared for her, my daughters had a great grandmother to cuddle and love them continually, but more importantly, the girls learned that the elderly are not disposable. As for me, perhaps the greatest lesson was not to give up hope.

Since 1994, Alice Lorraine Care Center has been thriving in Monroe. My goal has always been to surround each resident who enters with comfort, beauty and massive doses of love, as I did for my grandmother, Alice Lorraine. Perhaps it was for this reason she returned to make not only my life, but also the lives of countless others, so much more meaningful.

Thank you, Gram…I love you!

HEARTWARMING CARE
HOME CARE SERVICES
10209 Bridgeport Way SW Suite C-6
Lakewood, WA 98499
PHONE: 253.460.1574
WEBSITE: *www.heartwarmingcare.com*

Just the Two of Us

by RANDY WALDEN

JANET A HOME HEALTH NURSE HAS BEEN ATTENDING TO THE NEEDS OF HER parents, Ted and Sally. As the winter months are setting in with the short days and longer nights, she can no longer meet the demands of her parents (drop what you are doing we need this or that). Janet's employer has been understanding with her situation, but Janet is burning out. So, Janet placed a call for help, and that's where I come in. She explained to me that her parents are very proud folks, and her dad is not to keen on the idea of having outside help. Janet also explained that mom had dementia, but with dad helps is able to function. They need help with medication reminders, light housekeeping, prepare meals, and dad well he needs a bath.

So, with the information in hand it was time to meet Ted and Sally. As I enter the resident it was a very well maintain home, but the TV was turned up loud (Ted is hard of hearing). Janet introduced me to her parents, and Ted didn't wasted no time in giving me his rages to riches story. He saw himself as a self made man, and Sally was his loving bride. So, after a half hour it was my turn to explain how we could help him and Sally stay at home independently for as long as possible. Ted, had an objection for each point that I would raise, and I would prove him more information to clarify his objections. After we went round and around, Ted decided that he should give it a try. Service will be three hour in the morning and evening, three days a week.

As time move on over the next few months, Janet insisted that her parents have service seven days a week. Ted, had taken a likening to two of the caregivers, and they had taken to the both of them. As Sally's dementia declines, Ted is having trouble trying to provide care for her at nights, and it was decided that we at 24 hr live-in care. Maria, one of the caregivers said that she would be happy to provide them the live-in care. After month Sally's condition declined further, and she was put on hospice. This was taking a toll on the family, but Maria was by Sally's side, and this was a great comfort to Ted. Day's have pasted, Sally's was slipping away, Janet was checking in daily, Maria was having to provide more care to Ted, he was giving up as he watched the love of his live moving away from him. In the afternoon, Maria was singing to Sally as she passed away. Ted's heart was broken, but he had comfort in knowing that she was at home with him.

Preparation for Sally's funeral, the family had learned that Maria in her past life was a florist, so, that ask her if she could prepare flower arrangement. Maria was excited that family had asked her, and she jump right in. Janet's brother and his family came in from back east, and many of Sally's friends from church attended.

A couple of months later, Maria arrive at the home, and Ted did not answer the door. So, she got the hidden key went inside and found Ted on the floor, barely able to speak. It was a very cool night, and the heat of the house was off, so, she called 911 and Janet. Ted was taken to the hospital he had suffered a mild stroke. Things could have been worst if Maria was not coming over. Ted, stay another month in the hospital and the nursing home. He could not wait to come home, and again it was decided that he would need 24 hour care.

A month later Ted took a turn for the worst, he was place back into the hospital and then to the nursing home. This could have not come at a worse time for Janet, for she was to be married in a month, and she had to be out of time on business. She ask it Maria, could visit dad each day in the nursing home, and Maria gladly accepted. Upon Janet return, Ted was nearing the end, and I when to see Ted. When he heard my voice I told him that I would not charge him for my visit, we saw a smile. Janet, was trying to hold the tears back, I told her it was time for him to see Sally. Later, that evening Ted went to be with Sally.

HOME HELPERS
SAN RAMON AND DANVILLE CALIFORNIA
231 Market Place, Ste 21
San Ramon, CA 94583
PHONE: 925.236.2477
TOLL FREE: 1.888.99-HELPER
EMAIL: *robertJo@HomeHelpers.cc*

A Tribute to My Dad

by ROBERT JO, CSA

"WHY ARE YOU PUTTING ME IN THIS FACILITY?" THIS IS WHAT MY DAD IS ASKING as we were approaching a nursing home in San Diego. This was a decade ago and it still echoes in my mind and I can still hear my dad's voice clearly. I flew to San Diego from San Francisco to take my dad into a nursing home. We didn't tell him that we are putting him in a nursing home. When I arrived into my sister's house where my dad lives, he was smiling and very glad to see me. After the pleasantries, I told my dad that I want to drive him around which he wants to do. As we are approaching the nursing home, he was very much apprehensive and begged my sister and me to please not place him in that facility. Since he is semi-ambulatory, we took him in with a wheelchair. We waited till he settled in his room and go out of the facility as fast as we can. In the parking area, I remembered my sister and I were just sobbing and questioning ourselves if we did the right thing. It was a very heartbroken situation. I very much dreaded that moment until this day.

My dad had a very strong personality. He always gets what he wanted. He run a business successfully that placed us six children through college. He is very joyful and involved in community organization such as the Rotary club and the Gideon's club. He is very outgoing and fun to be with. One day, he was writing a check and he struggled to sign the check. He felt so weak and so we called the doctor. He had a stroke and was sent to the hospital right away. His left side of the body had been affected. His left arm was curled and he has to drag his left foot. He laughs and cries uncontrollably.

My sister is a nurse and decided to take care of dad. She and her husband took care of their two kids in spite of full time job as a nurse. With all the extracurricular activities, it is getting too much for her to take care of dad. Her husband is a very kind person who shared the responsibility of taking care of dad. He and dad go out almost every Saturday to see the garage sales in their neighborhood. It was the day that my dad looks forward to and often comes home very satisfied and contended - but not my sister. She would be very surprise on what they brought home but also the time taking care of dad is taking a toll on her and her family. So we had a family meeting that we need to share the burden of taking care of dad. I volunteered to take care of dad for a month. I was so excited that finally my dad will have the opportunity to play with my very young children. Boy I was wrong. It took me one week or so and I have to send dad back to my sister. It was a disaster between dad, small kids, full time job and housework.

We decided that we need to place dad in a nursing home to take the pressure out from my sister. We did not know of any other alternative and hoped that dad will be cared for properly. Dad had a couple more strokes and didn't take long in the nursing home before he went with the Lord.

When I learned about Home Helpers, I didn't hesitate to join the company. I believe that with this service, we can provide the family the option to have their loved ones stay at home while keeping that parent children relationship healthy. Home Helpers can provide a non-medical help at home for few hour a day or 24 hours a day, few days a week or 7 days a week. This would have been a very good option for my dad if we had known it before we placed him in the nursing home.

Having learned from my dad's situation, I believed that offering Home Helper's services meant a lot to my clients. I often hear from my clients that because of our care that the patient—spouse relationship had been better. Children of the patient are less stressed and are enjoying the time together. As one of my clients wrote "What more can I say? My anxiety level has gone way down. My husband and I can enjoy our times together. We have support." This is the reason why I loved my job and I wish I could have done this for my own dad.

SENIOR HELPERS
In-home companionship
and personal care assistance
28200 Orchard Lake Road, Suite 111
Farmington Hills, MI 48334
PHONE: 248.865.1000
WEBSITE: *www.seniorhelpers.com/location/2601*

In Our Home—My Mother's Choice

by BARBARA RODEN
Owner

PROVIDING CARE FOR A LOVED ONE CAN SOMETIMES BECOME TOO MUCH TO handle alone. Finding the right assistance may seem overwhelming. In-home care can provide support and assistance to meet your needs and those of your loved one.

My mom is a 94-year-old widow of twenty-five years. She and my dad moved out of town when they decided to enjoy a warmer climate. My father died one and one-half years later, so mom was living alone for the next twenty-five years. My brother would live nearby during the winter months, but he decided to move back to the Midwest about a year ago. We noticed that Mom's memory was starting to fade and we did not like the fact that she was living alone. Mom also has scoliosis and arthritis in her back which causes some pain, although she is on absolutely no medication. After discussing our concerns with her, we sold Mom's house and she moved in with me.

One day, Mom fell and fractured her hip. She spent a week in the hospital. It was recommended that she be admitted to a rehabilitation center, but Mom was afraid it would become a permanent situation. I work full-time and did not want her alone during the day. It wasn't hard to understand how Mom felt. She recently gave up her own home and was just beginning to settle in with me. To uproot her again would not be in her best interest. She has always been the happiest in comfortable surroundings. I also have personal experience with a nursing home setting. My husband was living in one for six months prior to his passing. They took excellent care of him, but I knew this was not the best solution for my mom. Faced with seeking alternative solutions, the hospital recommended Senior Helpers. I learned that the cost of in-home care is comparable to a nursing home or rehabilitation center, and felt fortunate that Mom has the funds available so she can remain at home.

I was quite impressed with Senior Helpers and the interview process. They talked to my mom and myself. Mom made it clear that she did not need a "babysitter." Senior Helpers suggested we hire a "housekeeper" instead. Mom accepted that idea. Barbara, the "housekeeper" handles the household duties such as cleaning and laundry. She also finds things for mom to do so she is busy and feels useful. Barbara has become a companion for my mom. Mom loves having her hair and nails done, so Barbara will take her as often as Mom wants to go.

Mom suffers from short-term memory loss, and I see signs of it getting worse. Despite these symptoms, Mom is still in amazing health for her age. I am so relieved to have Senior Helpers assisting with my mom. Although I see changes in her memory, I see many positive signs. Mom is happy! When Mom was home alone during the day, many times when I came home from work I would find Mom crying. This doesn't happen anymore. She does have bad days and becomes cranky, but Barbara is patient with her. Barbara helps keep the daily routine which is good for my mom. I am much happier and less stressed knowing that I don't have to worry whether something dangerous will happen or if Mom will wander off.

Over the past year, Mom has grown to accept Barbara as a friend, not our housekeeper. Our "housekeeper" arrangement with Senior Helpers has been a gift for both of us. I can go to work knowing Mom is safe and happy. Mom has a companion to fill her days and help her feel important by doing tasks together. I can now cherish our mother-daughter time and build on latest memories. I would recommend in-home care to anyone with similar needs. It is important to keep your loved ones in a home environment as long as possible. I did not have this opportunity with my husband, but I am truly blessed that I do with my mom. I know that as long as Mom's physical health is strong, she can continue living comfortable as she chooses—in our home.

COMFORT KEEPERS
245 Fairview Mall Drive, Suite 505
Toronto, Ontario, L4B 1Z3
PHONE: 416.663.2930
WEBSITE: *www.comfortkeepers.ca*

What a Difference the Right Caregiver Makes

by LAURIE SAUNDERS

DR. GOLDEN WAS USED TO OVERCOMING OBSTACLES. IN 1955 WHEN SHE announced that she wanted to become a doctor, everyone laughed at her and told her that women couldn't become doctors. She proved them wrong and became a successful Oncologist. She was well known for treating the whole patient, their physical and emotional needs.

How ironic, when she herself was diagnosed with stage 4 ovarian cancer and told she didn't have much time to live. She refused to accept that diagnosis and fought with everything she had. A year later she was doing well but needed some help. That's when her daughter, Anne, called me. She knew I was a cancer survivor myself and that as a result of my experience had started Comfort Keepers in Toronto, a company devoted to looking after those in need of help. Anne warned me that caring for her mother would not be easy: "my mother refuses to admit she needs help."

Well, it was hard going at first. Dr. Golden chased away the first four caregivers I sent her. However, we were committed to making the perfect match and sure enough Dr. Golden and Paula, the 5th caregiver, hit it off right from the start. They shared a love of books, and spent hours talking about the books they had enjoyed. As the weeks went by, and Dr. Golden started to fail, Paula would not only look after Dr. Golden's physical needs, but respond to her emotional needs, just as Dr. Golden had done for so many of her patients. Paula read to Dr. Golden every day and the 2 of them continued to talk about their favorite books.

One Sunday morning I received a call from Anne. Her mother was probably not going to last the day and Anne was going to spend the day with her. She asked me to let Paula know and cancel Paula's visit with Dr. Golden. Paula, however, felt so close to Dr. Golden that she asked if she too could spend the day with Dr. Golden. Paula told me that they had been through so much in the last year and she wanted to be with her right to the end. Anne and Paula spent the whole day by Dr. Golden's bed side, talking and sharing stories. Finally at 4pm, Anne said she was going to step out for a few minutes and get a coffee. Paula held Dr. Golden's hand, she looked into Paula's eyes and passed away peacefully.

Anne called me the next day and told me that at first she was upset that her mother had died when she left the room but then she realized that her mother was waiting for her to leave. Even in her last moments, Dr. Golden wanted to spare her daughter pain and did not want Anne to see her die. Anne told me she was so grateful, knowing that her mother had not died alone, but in the comfort of someone whom she loved and who loved her back.

I started my Comfort keepers office with the desire to give back to the community because of all of the help that I received when I was ill. It is moments like the one I described above, that tell me that I made the right decision.

COMFORT KEEPERS
245 Fairview Mall Drive, Suite 505
Toronto, Ontario, L4B 1Z3
PHONE: 416.663.2930
WEBSITE: *www.comfortkeepers.ca*

Enhancing the Quality of Life

by LAURIE SAUNDERS

SHORTLY BEFORE CHRISTMAS, BEATRICE CARSON, WAS ADMITTED TO THE HOSpital. Ever since her husband's stroke 2 years prior, Beatrice had devoted herself to looking after him, but now she was exhausted. Her husband, James, had been recovering well from his stroke but still had some trouble walking. Once Beatrice was admitted to the hospital, James announced that he could no longer walk. James's son called me and asked if I could send someone every day to make meals for James, keep the house clean, and take him out in his wheel chair. Because James was from Scotland and missed his wife, the son suggested a Scottish caregiver who was outgoing and talkative. We found the perfect caregiver, whose Scottish brogue matched James.

On December 23rd I received a call from James telling me that he hated his caregiver because she never stopped talking! He couldn't put up with her for one more day. Who was I going to get the day before Christmas? I called Elena. Elena is a wonderful, caring person, but she has a thick Russian accent. I had no idea how they would communicate, but I thought if we can just get through the holidays, I can find another Scottish caregiver after Christmas.

Much to my surprise, Elena and James were the perfect match. They may not have been able to speak to each other that well, but they had no problem communicating with each other. The respect and fondness they felt for each other was clear to everyone who saw them together.

Within 2 weeks, Elena had James walking again and the 2 of them walked every day, no matter what the weather was like.

Three months later Beatrice passed away. Elena was at James' side throughout the visitation and the funeral. He proudly introduced everyone to his "girl." To this day, James and Elena walk together every afternoon. Our goal at Comfort Keepers is to enhance our clients' quality of life, treat them as if they were a member of our family and help them stay independent. With Elena's help, James is the living embodiment of this goal.

COMFORT KEEPERS
252-39 Robertson Road
Ottawa, ON, Canada, K2H 8R2
PHONE: 613.820.1612
WEBSITE: www.comfortkeepers.ca

Lessons Learned from Nana

by SHARI WESTMAN

WHEN I WENT INTO BUSINESS FOR MYSELF, IT NEVER OCCURRED TO ME THAT I would learn more about the aging process, homecare and working with seniors than I did from my Nana.

My grandmother was grouchy. I know it's not nice or polite to seemingly disrespect an elderly person, or relative for that matter, particularly when you work with seniors daily. We called her "Grouchy Gran" when we talked about her, because she was simply miserable, often mean-spirited and her nickname helped us to cope as her family. Nana made it difficult to be around her and sadly, difficult to love her, even though we very much wanted to be around her more and love her more easily.

Nana was a fighter. Diagnosed with breast cancer in 1976, treated with a double mastectomy shortly thereafter and struggling with recurring tumors for the remaining 31 years of her life, she couldn't help but become a valiant fighter. I came to understand and even respect her grouchiness—she had been dealt with a very difficult hand. Nana was critical of the medical system, cynical about help and too tired, angry and worn out to really love her family, particularly since the death of her husband 25 years prior. She knew what she wanted, she knew how to get it and her expectations of those in her life, professionals, friends and family were high. But, she could never say "Thank-You", and she could never say "I Love You." In my early adult years, I found it easiest to stay away from her. When I became a young mother, with daughters of my own, it broke my heart that she had no interest in her few grandchildren and precious great-grandchildren. The Fighter who was my Nana, had worn me out.

Nana was steadfast in her conviction to life in her own home. For her, independence and dignity could only be found at home. She had many friends who resided in retirement homes, but leaving her home wasn't an option. Clever, capable and often creative, she managed to create a safe home environment that included a stair lift, a modified bathroom, she moved the laundry room out of the basement and up to the main level and acquired all sorts of assistive devices that made accommodations within her home easier.

Shortly after the birth of my second daughter, I opened a franchised office of an international senior's homecare agency. I had naturally inherited some my Nana's tenacity and determination. With a background in Human Resources, I developed a business by hiring wonderful, kind-hearted and committed caregivers to help enable our aging clients to live with greater independence on their own terms. If I couldn't connect to my own grandmother, perhaps I could with others.

About a year after I opened up my office, my dad called me worried about Nana. She was failing in health, having difficulty making meals, she wasn't driving any longer and she had for once, admitted to being lonely. He had talked with her and she had agreed to having a companion come into her home, three times a week to help her out, make meals with her, take her to appointments and visit with her. Dad wanted to know if I might have a companion with the fortitude to spend three afternoons a week helping Nana.

Not being close to grandmother of mine, and my newest client, I opted to treat her like I would every client. That's how she liked it. I went to her home to assess her needs and to outline her expectations of us. She was professional, cool and yet somehow, for the first time in many, many years, created an opportunity for us, Grandmother and Granddaughter to share. I spent hours with her on these repeat "assessments", learning from her, listening to her. She had spent many years volunteering with our local hospitals as a Palliative Care counselor and teacher. She had so much to offer, I so much to learn and for the first time we met as adults, keen to share.

My grandmother was one of the most difficult clients I've ever had, but truly the most rewarding personally. Her expectations were high and she remained difficult to please. However, with every caregiver that I have hired since, the bar, thanks to my Nana has been set, because I ask myself, could this person connect with Grouchy Gran and meet her standards? Two years after she started as a client with us, she passed away from a sudden heart attack. The day before her death, she spent the afternoon with her caregiver from my business, laughing, going to an appointment and then going out for lunch. At her funeral, the caregiver thanked me for introducing her to my grandmother as a client, because my Nana, had felt like a genuine grandmother to her.

COMFORT KEEPERS
5396 King James Way, Suite 210
Madison, Wisconsin
PHONE: 608.442.1898
WEBSITE: *www.comfortkeepers.com*

Personal Story of Alice Silversby

by STEPHEN P. RUDOLPH, FACHE, CSA

ALICE SILVERSBY WAS A RETIRED COLLEGE PROFESSOR OF MICROBIOLOGY. She had never married and was accustomed to doing what she wanted when she wanted.

As the signs of dementia began creeping up on her, she was adept enough to request that a friend become her Power of Attorney and guardian. She did not fear the future, but wanted to be prepared for it. As her disease state progressed, Alice knew she would have to make some sacrifices in order to stay in her own home. Her caregiver hired Comfort Keepers to provide round the clock care to Alice.

To say that Alice Silversby was a challenging elder is an understatement. She had a large home where she had lived independently for a long while and she did not want to share it with intruder caregivers.

There were a few episodes that are still talked about by Alice's caregivers. Alice's guardian had removed her car battery because she did not want Alice to drive. When Alice went into the garage to take a short trip in her car, it wouldn't start! She called a mechanic who told her the battery was not hooked up. The guardian was called and convinced Alice not to drive her car. The next day, Alice sent the caregiver on a bogus errand, then called the mechanic and had him hook up the car battery—and Alice had a wonderful afternoon driving around the city!

The second episode was a bit scary. It seems Alice had loved to hunt when she was younger and had a rifle in a locked cabinet. One day, unbeknownst to the caregiver, Alice opened her gun cabinet, grabbed her rifle, pointed it at the caregiver and told her to leave. When the police arrived, they discovered there was no ammunition in the house, but they confiscated the weapon. She could only smile sweetly at the cops.

Alice became more compliant as her disease state progressed, and although she did not become too unruly, she was still feisty. When she wanted something done, she wanted it done NOW. She loved to tend her garden, but had to be watched like a hawk, lest she wander to the neighbor' homes.

As Comfort Keepers continued to care for her, our caregivers developed a deep and abiding respect and admiration for Alice—and, over time, she for the caregivers!

All of us knew the stories about Alice and we all began to feel an incredible sense of pride and fulfillment in caring for her. As she slowly became weaker and started slipping faster, we developed a deeper love for this woman who had challenged us from the start. She became our elder role model—to go down swinging!

Because of Alice, and the stories of her that we still tell today, we are renewed with the strength of spirit, passion, affection, and devotion to duty that was reflected in the life's philosophy of Alice Silversby.

We continue to award one caregiver each year the Alice Silversby Award—for caring for the most challenging of our elders!

RIGHT AT HOME
11821 Parklawn Drive, Suite 302
Rockville, MD 20852
3231 Superior Lane Suite A21
Bowie, Maryland 20715
PHONE: 301.255.0066
WEBSITE: *info@rightathomemd.net*
RSA: #R2199

When One Door Closes, Another Opens

by WARREN MILLER

IN FEBRUARY OF 2004, LOREN AWOKE TO FIND HE HAD LOST THE DEAREST person in his life- his wife of 28 years. His grief was overwhelming. However, as one door closed for Loren, another one was opened. Loren had just retired and now that his beloved wife was gone, he needed something to fill his time. Loren did some hard and deep soul-searching. He found his thoughts continuing to drift back to his wife and the part of her life that had brought much happiness and fulfillment to her over the past few years, working as a Right at Home caregiver. If it meant so much to her, maybe it would help fill the empty void she left when she passed away and bring the same fulfillment to me, thought Loren. With some trepidation, Loren opened a new door—one that has led him down a road of healing and personal fulfillment. "It is my way to give back to others, just as my wife chose to spend her last years helping others." Loren has provided comfort and dignity to many individuals during their lives and has in-turn gained hope, strength and peace. Loren hopes to pass along a bit of that strength and hope to the lives of those he touches as a caregiver.

Thirty-one year old Brian is one of those individuals. Brian has been paralyzed from the chest down since he was 19 years old after surviving a car accident. Following the accident, Brian spent months in physical therapy to regain use of his arms and hands and continues therapy on a regular basis. Brian currently lives with his parents Ron and Suzie who have assisted Brian since his accident. Every day presents its own set of challenges for Brian, who requires assistance with his daily personal needs such as bathing, dressing and getting in and out of his wheelchair. Loren comes in each morning and helps Brian get ready for his day, ensuring that Brian is clean, safe and comfortable.

Once Brian's personal care needs are met, he is able to function on his own throughout the day. The regular visits by Loren, the Right at Home Caregiver, mean a lot to Brian; they allow him to maintain some dignity in his life. Although Brian has lost much of his physical function, he has not lost his will to live and enjoy life. He still partakes in many of the things he enjoyed in the past like fishing, racing spectator cars, video games, movies, using the computer and traveling. "I adapted pretty quickly," says Brian. "I don't let anything slow me down, I just keep telling myself I can't get depressed about it and I have to keep pushing forward."

Loren is now part of the inspiration that helps Brian face each day. On mornings when Brian isn't feeling especially motivated, he knows Loren will soon be there to help him get a start on his day, offer him encouragement and raise his spirits. Brian recently began therapy to use leg braces. Brian knows it will be a long and difficult journey that will require months of therapy and hard work, but with caregivers like Loren to support him, Brian feels his dream is within reach. Brian's family, have used the assistance of Right at Home caregivers for the past five years, say that it has now become a natural part of their routine. "The caregivers do everything to help him take care of his personal care in the mornings and evenings," says Susie. "It's a huge help to me and I think Brian really likes someone else coming in to help so he doesn't feel like a burden to me. It's a very comfortable situation." "Loren is very good with Brian. He is reliable and you can tell he really cares about his work," says Susie. "I don't do this for the money, I do it because I enjoy it," says Loren. "My clients are my priority. When you do a good job and everything goes right and you know you've helped someone, it sure feels good."

SUE HAVILAND
3604 Advocate Court
Jarrettsville, Maryland 21084
EMAIL: *sue@asksuehaviland.com*
PHONE: 443.677.0389
WEBSITE: *www.asksuehaviland.com*

Reverse Mortgages— Real Life Solutions for Senior Homeowners

by SUE HAVILAND

IN MY 7 OR 8 YEARS IN THE REVERSE MORTGAGE BUSINESS, I HAVE BEEN SO FORtunate to see this fantastic program help so many families, it's hard to select one story to tell. The lady whose story I will recount illustrates just one example of how a reverse mortgage can truly enhance a senior's life.

I received a call one afternoon with a request for reverse mortgage information. This conversation started out fairly routine, until the person identified herself. She was from an in home care agency. And she was inquiring about one of her clients at the request of the family. This lady was a long time client and clearly had a place in the hearts of the caregivers at this agency. Her funds to pay for the care she enjoyed were running low and the other family members lived too far away to help. Nor did they want to uproot her from her home where she had lived for over 40 years. The reverse mortgage appeared to be a good option, and could provide the means to pay for her care, but I had no idea just how much it would help her.

On the day I met her for her reverse mortgage application, she was sitting in her living room watching from the window as she did each day. Her caregiver had already been to visit, and she'd had her lunch. I noticed that she was wearing a little shamrock pin. It was St. Patrick's Day and she told me her caregiver brought it for her. She told me about when she first purchased the home with her husband who had passed many years ago. She recounted many details of their years together in the home and it was clear to me that this lady really did love this home and wanted to remain there.

Once the reverse mortgage was completed, I kept in touch with this lady and received a lovely note of gratitude from her family. They credited the in home care agency for helping them find a solution when they otherwise might have been faced with a difficult decision about having to move this senior from the home she loved. The reverse mortgage did in fact allow her to live in her home for the remainder of her life.

SENIOR HELPERS
In-home companionship
and personal care assistance
28200 Orchard Lake Road, Suite 111
Farmington Hills, MI 48334
PHONE: 248.865.1000
WEBSITE: *www.seniorhelpers.com/location/2601*

On a Mission for Uncle John

by BARBARA RODEN
Owner

JOHN HAS ALWAYS BEEN INDEPENDENT. AT FOURTEEN, HE JOINED THE ARMY because he said "my four sisters were driving him crazy." Two weeks before his eighteenth birthday the Army learned his age and he was discharged. He re-enlisted when he turned eighteen. Years later, John joined the Navy, and then the Air Force, from which he retired in 1970. John was the navigator on eight of the eleven Apollo missions.

We think about our aging loved ones from time to time, but no one really understands how it affects a family until faced with the situation. Looking back over the last few years, John's family saw signs of him becoming more isolated and depressed. It was not obvious at any given moment because he was so independent having been on his own since 1970 and traveling extensively all his life. Although John was living in Arizona, he remained close to family. He always came to visit for Christmas, which was definitely a highlight of the holidays. John was full of life and such the charmer. He lit up a room by his presence alone. The family became concerned when John planned his annual Christmas visit, but did not show up or call. After seeing pictures of John, the family realized he was not the same person.

After being diagnosed with frontal lobe dementia, John moved in with a relative, but the situation was not in his best interest. Ron (John's nephew) and Mary stepped in a year ago. They moved Uncle John to their home in Michigan. Mary was caring for him, but was also working full-time. They needed help and began interviewing several nursing homes and assisted living centers. The emotions of finding the best caregiver for Uncle John became overwhelming. After repeatedly reaching dead ends, Mary was referred to Senior Helpers. She felt an instant connection with Barbara Roden, owner of Senior Helpers, because Barbara shared the same values and also had a personal connection dealing with Alzheimer's.

Ron and Mary are extremely pleased with Shay, Uncle John's caregiver. Uncle John feels safe living with Ron and Mary, and is now equally comfortable with Shay. It is reassuring to know that while Ron and Mary are working, Uncle John is receiving companionship and care. Although her first priority is Uncle John, Shay helps Mary with household chores, keeps her organized, and helps the family function as a unit. It allows Mary and Ron more time to spend together.

John loves to be outdoors. He will sit alone and listen to the birds, or he and Shay will chat. He enjoys talking about his days in the military, and Shay enjoys listening, no matter how many times she has heard the story before. John has a great sense of humor and is a real comedian. He also enjoys going out to dinner and the movies. John has always been a shopper and big spender. He loves to shop especially for women. He likes to buy them his favorite Joy perfume. John was such a charmer; he could charm the pants off anyone. He was, and still is, ready with a smile and a compliment.

It is not easy caring for someone with dementia. Every day is the same; it is just like the movie, Groundhog Day. Ron and Mary could record a daily conversation with John and replay it daily. They continuously look for a glimmer of change. They cherish the times when it does happen, like the day he deviated from his daily Nutty Buddy ice cream cone and wanted to go out for ice cream. Uncle John definitely has bad days, which are even predictable—every ten days, but Shay works hard to engage in conversation and make Uncle John more comfortable. She keeps Mary and Ron apprised when Uncle John is having a bad day, so they are more prepared when they arrive home. That in itself gives the couple a great deal of comfort and peace of mind.

Ron and Mary feel successful in their mission to find the best care for Uncle John, who also seems to still be on a mission—a mission to retain his independence and enjoy life.

SENIOR HELPERS
In-home companionship
and personal care assistance
28200 Orchard Lake Road, Suite 111
Farmington Hills, MI 48334
PHONE: 248.865.1000
WEBSITE: *www.seniorhelpers.com/location/2601*

Independence for Life

by BARBARA RODEN
Owner

BILL WAS A SELF-MADE BUSINESS OWNER. TECHNICALLY, HE STILL IS, ALTHOUGH his son now runs the business. Five years ago, his wife passed away. Being "a man of the 1950s," Bill didn't know how to take care of himself. His wife did the shopping, cooking, cleaning, and laundry. He could not do things for himself, nor did he want to learn, so Bill's family members took over those roles. Because of his health issues, it was essential that he eat properly and take his medications accurately and regularly. The family made lists for him to check off when he ate meals and took his medicines, and someone would check on him daily. They hired a driver to take him to appointments, and a cleaning person as well. Even with the additional help, however, caring for Bill and maintaining their own family schedules were causing overwhelming emotional strain and stress.

Over the last several years, Bill struggled with several health issues. He is a diabetic, has a pacemaker, and had bypass surgery. About two years ago, the family noticed that Bill was declining mentally. He was forgetting to take his medications and insulin, did not have good hygiene, and was less stable in his walking. Bill was suffering from frontal temporal dementia. Soon thereafter, he was admitted to the hospital for a heart-related condition. After being released, he went to a rehabilitation facility to recuperate. Once a social man, he started keeping to himself and lost motivation. Bill was not happy and wanted to go home. Knowing that he would not be able to live completely on his own again, the family began exploring various options. Bill was adamant about remaining in his own home and the family felt it would be the best environment for him as well. When weighing in-home care versus other alternatives, they found the costs to be comparable. The family began asking for referrals, and selected four companies to interview. Their main concern was that the company and caregivers were bonded and insured and would give reliable, compassionate care. Senior Helpers was clearly the choice for them.

Although Bill was part of the decision process, he was still hesitant at first. He had always been the "pillar" of the family, so adjusting to supplemental care was a little difficult for him. In just a short time, though, he became quite comfortable and content. He is happy in his own surroundings. One of Bill's favorite things is sitting in his living room looking out at the lake. When asked why, he responds that he has worked hard for many years, and has earned the right to enjoy the view!

Bill's caregivers handle housekeeping, laundry, grocery shopping, and meals, making sure he takes his medicines, monitoring his vital signs, assisting with grooming, driving him to appointments, and helping him attend events and functions that are important to him. On occasion they will even go out to eat. The caregivers have attended family gatherings with Bill (picnics, parties, Easter breakfast) and are then available to take him home when he is "ready." When Bill has a doctor appointment, the caregiver will help him get showered and dressed, and drive him to the appointment where they meet a family member who is then free to focus on Bill's appointment with the doctor.

The family feels blessed to have found Senior Helpers. Much of the stress and worry they had been experiencing before is gone. Just knowing he is not alone is important; since he no longer drives, the daily companionship helps stimulate his mind. Sometimes a family member will stop by and find Bill and his caregiver watching a game show and shouting the answers at the television. The family is confident that Bill is getting the best possible care while remaining in familiar surroundings. They can now spend quality time with him because they no longer have to be the primary caregivers. Bill's family is delighted with Senior Helpers and believes the company offers an invaluable service. Most importantly, Bill is happy, content, and looks forward to living as he chooses—in his home.

SENIORS AT HOME
3973 8th Avenue
San Diego, CA 92103
PHONE: 619.291.4663
EMAIL: *staff@seniors-at-home.net*
WEBSITE: *www.seniors-at-home.net*

Francine's Life Has Changed

by SHIELA KORN

WHEN I FIRST MET FRANCINE SHE WAS IN BED, IN A DARK ROOM, IN THE FETAL position. I just sat beside her and read out loud from a book of poetry that I found in the house.

Her sister, who lived in Tucson, and her brother who lived in Hawaii had been visiting after not seeing her for several months. They called Seniors At Home because they didn't want to place her in a facility. When her Alzheimer's disease had first been diagnosed, she told her family she wanted to be taken care of at home. Francine had worked hard all her life and diligently saved so there was enough to pay for home care. Her sister and brother realized that Francine had become isolated because no one had arranged for help to come in. Now was the time to get that started. They arranged for a caregiver to come in 6 hours a day, 7 days a week.

Four years ago, Francine was going out every day. She would often go to the country club or a favorite restaurant. Up until 5 years ago she was a docent at the art museum. Folks would love to hear her talk about Vangogh, Matisse or Renoir.

So I sat beside her and read and realized that her body relaxed. I told her who I was and that I would get her cleaned up and get her something to eat. She didn't say a word but her body language told me she was pleased. I brought a basin of warm water and wash cloth over by the bed and proceeded to gently cleanse her body. I rubbed lotion on her back, arms and legs and helped her into clean clothes. I helped her up and then I changed the bed sheets. She was sitting up in a comfortable, recliner that was in her room. I prepared a simple meal and fed it to her. We sat together for a long time while I read, played the radio and just held her hand. When it was time for me to go, she smiled and said, "Will you be coming back?"

Seniors At Home has been providing care now for Francine for over a year. We have become her extended family. Her caregiver, Carol, calls her "Grandma" and she just smiles from ear to ear. When her sister and brother come to visit they are amazed at how well she is doing. She gets out to the park and goes to the zoo. She looks well nourished and her house is bright, clean and airy. She is getting to doctors appointments and occasionally seeing some old friends.

GENTOG, LLC
PHONE: 503.639.2600
EMAIL: *www.gentog.com*

A Place for Evangeline

by MARCIE JONES
Co-founded Gentog with her best friend Muriel (Murt) Bickett

EVANGELINE IS A FORMER TEACHER, WHO ENJOYED AN ADVENTUROUS LIFE. SHE traveled extensively, and taught children in remote Montana. She is generally sweet natured, although dementia causes confusion and fears that lead to occasional stubbornness these days. Her adult children take turns caring for Evangeline, although her daughter Linda shoulders most of the responsibility. Evangeline now lives with Linda and her husband, and requires full-time supervision.

Evangeline used to attend programs at the local Senior Center, but can no longer carry a conversation or find her way. The Senior Center informed Linda that she would not be able to attend the center alone. Her children searched for a good Adult Day Program where she would be comfortable, but she has had difficulty adjusting to them. She was not able to participate in the discussions and activities at the first program, and they suggested that the family should find a different program for her. Linda and her siblings continued their search for the right place for mom, and they found Gentog. Linda hoped that because there was an intergenerational program at Gentog that her mother's former teaching experiences would help her to adjust there.

Evangeline is adjusting very well today. At Gentog it's OK that Evangeline starts a sentence, but cannot finish it. Gentog staff helps to fill in the blanks.

Most of her elderly friends have similar difficulties, and simply smile and nod. Evangeline can't follow the rules of games like dominoes, but she loves being Lisa's partner and winning most games she plays. Luck is often on their side, and Evangeline enjoys being able to participate in the games with everyone else.

Evangeline is physically well, and enjoys walking with the elder friends that use walkers. She often pushes a wheelchair on group walks, helping her to stay with the group rather than wandering. It also allows her to be kind and helpful, as she's always been. Her smile and gentle nature make her popular among the other elders in this program.

The magic of her days at Gentog happen when the kids come in. Twice a day the children from the childcare room come to visit the "Grandmas and Grandpas." Evangeline does not have grandchildren of her own, but she has a natural bond with the kids. Her love of children and delight in playing with them make her a favorite of the kids. Her giggles can be heard as two-year-old Benjie offers her a pretend cup of tea. She shares a book with four-year-old Patty, who doesn't care that not all of the words are read. They simply chuckle over the funny pictures. And how she loves to sing with the children! Tapping their toes and holding hands, Evangeline and three-year-old Skylar enjoy a rowdy rendition of "I've Been Working on the Railroad." When it's time for Hokie Pokie, Evangeline doesn't always sit and watch the children…she often joins the circle to sing, laugh and "turn herself around"! The children all love the days that Evangeline visits, as they love to share that laughter with her.

Evangeline doesn't remember the name Gentog. She can't tell her family what she does there each day. She's not always happy when her daughter tells her it's time to leave home in the morning. But Linda knows that her mom is not safe left home alone, and she encourages Evangeline that she'll enjoy where she's going. Evangeline pouts as they drive along, but as the pull into the parking space in front of the Gentog doors, she smiles. "Oh. I love this place." Lisa greets her at the door. Little Skylar waves enthusiastically from across the room. Both Evangeline and Linda smile. This day will be another good one.

GENTOG, LLC
PHONE: 503.639.2600
EMAIL: *www.gentog.com*

Good for Families

by MARCIE JONES

Co-founded Gentog with her best friend Muriel (Murt) Bickett

CHARLOTTE BEGAN NOTICING HER MOTHER'S CHANGES IN THE FALL. MADELINE wasn't able to remember to do the simple tasks like preparing her own meals. She no longer enjoyed reading novels because she couldn't hold onto the story's concept from one page to the next. Her conversations were repeated over and over again.

Madeline moved into Charlotte's home after Christmas. Charlotte and her siblings decided that mom would be happiest living with one of them rather than in a strange place. Everyone agreed that Charlotte's home was best suited for mom, and Charlotte gladly took on the responsibility. The adjustment to having her mom present in her home every day took awhile. Everyone dearly loved Madeline, so they did what they could to help out…at first. As the months passed, though, Charlotte's siblings and children became busy with their own lives, and they visited less often. Charlotte found herself spending almost every day at home with her mom, and they both began to feel isolated.

Charlotte began to feel resentful of her duties, and that made her feel very guilty. She loved her mother very much, and wanted to provide the very best care. It was her duty, as the eldest daughter in the family, after all. But still…

One day, while reading through a "Boomer" newspaper, Charlotte saw an article about Adult Day Services. A place to take her mom during the day occasionally so she could enjoy a shopping day with friends or even a day in her house alone for awhile was very tempting. She began searching the internet for Adult Day Programs in her area. She found one that seemed promising, even intriguing. It promised a day of activities with other seniors as well as time with young children…an intergenerational daycare program. She made an appointment to take her mom for a trial day.

Charlotte took Madeline to Gentog, and left her there with some apprehension. What if her mom became confused and scared? She'd promised to keep mom at home, and worried that Madeline would feel abandoned. While Charlotte spent the day running errands and worrying, she didn't know that Madeline spent the morning with other seniors in a coffee club. She joined in with the group practicing seated Tai Chi. She went for a walk in the sunshine with two other ladies. She had a delicious lunch, then joined the other women for a reading club where the Activities Director read short, funny stories and everyone shared some laughs and reminisced about when their children were young.

Ten minutes ahead of her appointed return time, Charlotte enteres the doors of Gentog and looks around the Family Room for her mom. She notices a gentleman sitting by the fireside in a recliner, feet moving slightly to the sound of soft music. The sound of giggles from the corner of the room draw her attention. There, on a large wrap-around couch sits her mother and several other "grandmas and grandpas." Interspersed amongst them are staff members and several young children. Each child is sharing a story book with an elder friend. The children are intrigued by the books, and many cuddle into the side of their "grandma." She notices that some pairs read quietly…some giggle as they turn the pages…some are very engrossed in their books. The common thread between them is joy. Charlotte spots her mom in the middle of the couch, laughing and reading a story with an adorable little girl. In that moment she knows that she's found the right place for her mom. She becomes comfortable with the idea of bringing Madeline here for visits so she can have some free time. She knows that they will both enjoy their days apart, and their evenings back together will be more relaxed and happy as a result.

As Charlotte walked towards the couch, she notices a phrase stenciled on the wall. She smiles to herself as she whole-heartedly agrees. *Intergenerational Daycare…Good for Children…Good for Seniors…Good for Families.*

**CARE-TO-GO HOME CARE
AND TRAVEL COMPANIONS**
PHONE: 480.284.8611
TOLL-FREE: 800.818.0407

What In-Home Care Giving Really Should Be for Your Loved One

by BETH BATES

THIS IS A STORY OF LOUISE T., A PERSON EVEN YOU COULDN'T HELP BUT LOVE. She'd inherited a beautiful home from her mother in Scottsdale, Arizona. Surprisingly, the unforeseen death of her beloved mother occurred on April 29, 2007 and by mid December, stress had taken its toll. Notably, her hair became brittle and began falling out.

She thought it was because of the deep mourning for her mother's death, but after visiting her doctor, Louise was then diagnosed with cancer. Saddened by this news, Louise's schedule became riddled with radiation and chemotherapy treatments; and after such treatments, Louise became weak to her core. Yet, she was trying to handle everything on her own.

Louise, being as incredibly self-reliant and independent as she is, was determined to take care of herself. Her brother could see she was in need of help, but he was unable to give the motherly care she needed. So, he sat her down and with all the love in his heart he said, *"Louise, it's time we get you some in home health care."*

At that time, she couldn't see how important it was to have that kind of support, but as she looked around at her house, she knew her brother was right.

ENTER CARE-TO-GO IN-HOME CAREGIVERS...

Once Louise and I met, we quickly got into the routine of radiation and chemotherapy treatments. After each session, I would make a light lunch, shop for food at a local grocer, and then prepare dinner. We so enjoyed each other's company, laughter, edgy conversations and inspiration spiced up our long emotional days. I tell you, her treatments took a toll on her strength, but not on her spirit.

Well, after several months of taxing treatments Louise was more than ready to get back to her apartment in California. By now she was using a walker and a wheelchair just to get around. I mentioned to her that we, Care-To-Go, could escort her back to California and with a smile, Louise welcomed the idea.

WE'RE GOING BACK TO CALI...

So we were off... to the airport, through the baggage area, through airport security, onto the airplane for a relaxing flight, and to Louise's apartment in California. While there, I set up her apartment following her personal directions, prepared a welcome home meal, and then rested in her comfortable apartment. Louise then looked at me and told me she was grateful for the support and realized she could have never done this on her own.

After some time, Louise moved from her apartment to a home she'd purchased in California. But the day she moved in to her new home, she fell and fractured her hip. For the next four months during her healing, Louise took residence in an assisted living facility.

IT'S NOT WHAT YOU KNOW, BUT WHO YOU KNOW!

Since Louise and I had a wonderful friendship, we kept tabs on each other. And again when she was ready to go back home, she called me to help her get settled in her new home.

We came up with a plan of action that involved:

- Unpacking and organizing her home
- Maintaining her physical therapy schedule

- Scheduling a handyman to revamp her bathroom
- Planning dinners with her son Steve (where laughter was definitely the main course)
- Plus other daily living activities which had to be accomplished

Well, after about 10 days it was time to head back to Phoenix, but we weren't finished yet. I'd taken pictures of the contents of her mother's home back in Scottsdale, Arizona and made two catalogs, one for her one for me.

We went through the catalogs determined what she'd like me to send her after her mother's home was sold. When the time came, the furniture and smaller items were packed and sent to her new home in California.

In conclusion, Care-To-Go assisted a person in much need of aid. We all know someone who has had the misfortune of a physical / mental illness, a physical condition, or just plain old age. Regardless, in-home care is just a phone call away.

OREGON ELDER OPTIONS
IN HOME CARE, INC.
PO Box 33672
Portland, OR 97292-3672
PHONE: 503.255.2377
WEBSITE: *www.oregonelderoptions.org*

Mr. Lloyd's Favorite Visitor

by RIKI SOPHER
Administrator

I FIRST MET MR. LLOYD IN HIS HOME AFTER RECEIVING A CALL FROM HIS DAUGHTER, Judy, asking if I would assess him for In Home Care. Mr. Lloyd was an 85 year old who had suffered several minor falls at home. Recently, he had been neglecting his personal hygiene for fear of falling in the bathroom. "One thing you have to know about my Dad," Judy told me laughing, "is that he is fiercely independent and as stubborn as an ox."

Mr. Lloyd told me that he was concerned about having someone come in to his life and "take over." Although I could clearly see a need for this gentleman to have the assistance of a caregiver, it was equally apparent to me that, for him, the decision to have help was equivalent to sacrificing the last vestige of his independence. We also talked about his plan for the future. "I don't ever want to go to one of those places for old people." he told me, "I want to stay here, at home, until I die."

Mr. Lloyd and I were able to reach an agreement; He would allow me to introduce a caregiver and, if he liked her, he would "tolerate" having her visit twice a week, "but only for an hour." He did not want the caregiver to help him with bathing, "But," he said, "It will satisfy Judy that someone is checking in on me." I introduced my employee Karen to him that Friday. Karen was a patient, bright young woman with a cheerful attitude and an easy sense of humor. Within a few minutes of their introduction, Karen and Mr. Lloyd were talking about fishing and the proper way to prepare freshly caught trout.

Though she would gently offer her assistance, for the first two weeks Mr. Lloyd adamantly refused to allow Karen to do anything for him beyond pouring and serving a Coke. Gradually, he became more comfortable with Karen and would share with friends and family that he looked forward to her visits twice a week. She just continued to be that steady, quiet presence in Mr. Lloyd's life. Karen showed up for every scheduled shift with positive attitude and a "fish tale" to share.

One evening Judy phoned me to tell me that her Dad had fallen and fractured his hip. Three days after surgery he was discharged from the hospital to a skilled nursing facility for rehabilitation therapy.

When I visited him in the nursing home, I was surprised to see Mr. Lloyd in his hospital bed, the blinds closed, and staring at the wall. In talking with the Discharge Planner, I discovered that, since his admission to the facility earlier in the week, Mr. Lloyd had refused to participate in therapy, was not eating and was throwing staff members out of his room. "I don't know what else we can do," she told me, "we're going to have to discharge him. I guess he could go to an adult foster care or a long term care facility. He certainly can't return home in this condition." I returned to Mr. Lloyd's room, sat down by his bed and asked, "What can I do?" He looked past me and said dully, "No one here cares. Everyone is in a hurry. They tell me when to eat, when to wake up and when to sleep. It's like being in a prison. I just want to go home."

The following day, Judy met me at the facility. Together we created a plan for Karen to come to the facility three times a week at a time chosen by Mr. Lloyd to work with him on his exercise program. When Judy talked to her Dad about our idea, he brightened up immediately. Within a week and a half, the Discharge Planner telephoned me to say that there had been marked improvement in Mr. Lloyd's progress. He was actively participating in his therapy routine, had begun joking with members of the staff, and was getting out of bed and dressed on a daily basis.

Mr. Lloyd was able to return to his own home within 12 weeks of fracturing his hip. With support from a team of amazing caregivers who were able to look past the gruff exterior and honor the man inside, he remained in his home for the rest of his life.

COMFORCARE HOME SERVICES
35325 Date Palm Drive, Suite 253
Cathedral City, CA 92234
655 Montgomery Street, Suite 540
San Francisco, CA 94108
PHONE: 800.993.2945
WEBSITE: *www.comforcare.com*

My Guardian Angel

by LISA MARIE BLASKIE, RN, CCM, CSA

I FIRST MET SUZANNE AND HER ADULT SON BILL ON A SATURDAY IN MARCH of 2003. She was 85 years old and had been independent for most of her life but had a fall about six months ago and following hospitalization was currently in a rehab facility. Suzanne was an alert woman full of life and did let us know about her political persuasion and her life experiences. Over the coming months we were to get used to her way of directing others that came from her long career as the guest relations manager at a well known upscale hotel in San Francisco. Her son Bill had recently gone through a less than positive experience with care giving issues with his wife's mother who passed away almost a year before. That experience included having multiple caregivers, less than adequately trained and poor follow-up with agency supervision.

I talked with Suzanne and Bill about my own experience with my mother who was living in Michigan who was still in her home with my brother. Personal stories have always been important to me as I developed a relationship with family and clients. I was able to go to the next step working with the family to secure an apartment where she could have a degree of independence with our care.

Over the next two weeks I worked with the family to secure an apartment with the necessary lay out for a wheelchair bound person to be able to live in her new home. We were able to provide the necessary changes for her to be self sufficient in her apartment. Suzanne was able to inspect and sign off on her new home. Just before her Rehab release Suzanne fell at the Rehab that caused an open wound on her lower leg. That was not to stop her from her goal of going to her new home but would play into events later.

Suzanne moved into her new apartment and she settled into her routine. Bill and the rest of the family left to go back to the east coast. Suzanne would always articulate her needs clearly and she paid attention to the smallest details. Attempts to change bad habits particularly smoking would be problematic for the rest of her life. Suzanne's clear mind and her ability to control situations provided us with an opportunity to grow in trust slowly and we settled into a routine of meals, exercise walks, showers. Getting her to change her habits would always be a problem but we worked together to make sure she was well cared for.

What changed the degree of trust and allowed her to listen and to seek out my advice was her leg wound from the fall which was still being cared for by a visiting wound care nurse two times a week. Suzanne was diabetic, had heart problems and showed signs of poor circulation in her feet so proper wound care was a major concern. Two weeks later I visited Suzanne in her apartment to discuss her care thus far and she asked me to look at her wound. I removed the bandages and I encountered an obvious red inflammation extending out and the yellow drainage in a 4 week wound that situation warranted a visit to the emergency room immediately.

When we met the emergency room doctor he took one look at the wound and after asking me some questions told Suzanne she should keep me close because if I hadn't brought her to him the results might mean the loss of her leg. Two hours later following treatment and tests she was released and given at home instruction on the wound care.

My relationship with her changed she told me to call her Suzy and from that day on her referred to me as her "guardian angel" who saved her from possibly losing her leg. My interaction with Suzy after this episode was always interesting, I learned a lot from her about famous people and their secrets that she shared with me. Suzy even became my business advisor as she was a great proof reader and I put her to good use.

SANITASOLE
Marco Island's Premier Place for Senior Health
218 S Barfield Dr
Marco Island, FL 34145
PHONE: 239.394.9931
EMAIL: *probinson@sanitasole.net*
WEBSITE: *www.sanitasole.net*

My Mom: On the Wings of Angels

by PAULA CAMPOSANO-ROBINSON, RN
Vice President of Clinical Services

WHEN A FAMILY MEMBER PASSES AWAY IT IS AS THOUGH A PIECE OF ONE'S SELF has also faded away. As a child, I looked at my parents as though they were invincible; they kept me safe, warm, fed, loved and secure. However, as an adult, I came to terms with the reality that even my parents were vulnerable; a difficult realization as I thought I had a fairy tale life—we would live forever happily ever after.

Fast forward a few decades: December 30, 1999. It was a typical winter night for Marco Island; cold enough to make Floridians need a heavy jacket and warm enough to lure winter visitors to flock our beaches. I had just settled in bed after a long work day but got a phone call from my dad which was most unusual - it was after midnight. His soft, almost stuttering, hesitant voice was cracking; I was trembling as I listened. I thought something had happened to him, but before I could ask, dad stated "I'm at the emergency room in Naples; I think your mother had a stroke." (Long pause), I quickly responded, "Dad, I will be right there, everything will be okay."

I have little recollection of the drive to Naples Community Hospital; the adrenaline was rushing through my body so quickly that my eyes were blurry.

Mom had not been ill; at 72 years young she had the normal aches and pains of healthy aging, but a stroke? It couldn't be!

When I arrived at the hospital, my instincts as a nurse promptly took over. The emergency room is an imposing atmosphere for everyone; for those who are worried and scared, it is darn right horrible. There are bright lights, nurses pushing, pulling emergency carts through the halls, people crying, and the concerned looks of doctors who scatter from one cubicle to another. Dad was standing in a corner bewildered, glancing around the E.R., pacing, shaking his head in total disbelief. I ran up to him, threw my arms around him and assured him that everything would be okay.

If only I had the power to make everything okay…

I anxiously went to hug Mom, on a gurney with a tube in her nose, a lightweight vest on to keep her from trying to get out of bed and both wrists in soft restraints. I immediately asked that they remove the restraints as I promised to be at her side.

Mom was awake, with slurred garbled, almost inaudible speech and paralyzed on her left side. As an experienced RN who has cared for innumerable stroke victims for decades, I was trying desperately to maintain my composure and reassure her that she would be okay. I kept thinking that with all my training as a health care professional, I am totally helpless. I can only offer my mom comfort and give back to her the love she had always shown me.

With a myriad of hospital specialists tending to Mom, Dad and I stayed close until she was finally assigned a hospital bed in the neurological ICU. I called my brother Steven, and asked him to come to the hospital right away - Moms' condition was serious. My sister, Jean, also a nurse came from Boston and over the next few days we took shifts in managing the care of mom along with updating our family members who were also arriving from out of town; my youngest sister, Donna was out of the country but she made it to the hospital so our family was united.

I was determined to be involved in all aspects of mom's care; the staff didn't hamper my efforts or those of my family members. The days passed painfully slow; mom was slipping away and there was nothing we could do. Jean and I gave her baths, changed her linens and we chatted to her about anything and everything. We turned her, combed her hair, fluffed her pillows, wet her lips, and held her hand often laying our heads on the side rail of the hospital bed from physical and emotional exhaustion.

It was shortly after her admission to NICU that mom slipped into a coma. Those last verbal exchanges and laughs in the ER were now ever most precious to my Dad and me. She lay lifeless from a hemorrhagic stroke with only occasional involuntary movements now.

We knew in our hearts our mother, and Dad's partner of 50 plus years was not going to live with any quality of life. Dad agreed that Mom never wanted to be on life support so she was moved to a private room outside the NICU. My sister and I continued our nursing rituals but it became more and more difficult now that we were preparing Mom and ourselves for her imminent death. Tears of sorrow spilled over into the room.

But like strong, courageous eagles, we gathered around telling mom how much we love her, how much she means to us and that we would miss her. We took turns lying next to her in the bed while stroking her hair, laughing, crying and playing my dad's recorded music (He is a self-taught musician and has a wonderful voice), and telling comical and often embarrassing stories of our youth. We called our family priest, knowing that she would soon be off on an angel's wing.

I vividly remember as the end was approaching, Jean was on watch. We were all sprawled around the room; Jean shook me awake and said, "It won't be long, Paula." I then woke Dad, and the others and we all hovered over mom's bed. Dad held mom's hand and just starred at her, holding back tears. It was beautiful, yet heartbreaking.

Oh, mom, if only…

On this early morning, January 6, 2000, mom spread her wings and we said our final goodbyes.

As a teenager and young adult, we can't wait for the day to come when we can leave the nest and soar on our own. If only we humans realized at a young age that life passes all too quickly—if only I had more time with mom.

Her nicknames were: Grammy Eileen, Gram, "Mother" Mom, and "Roper" from the popular television series, "Three's Company." Most endearing was the pet name my dad gave her. He called her "Eileena." She was the frugal shopper, a devoted wife, dads' cheerleader, and a beautiful, selfless woman.

After a Christian Mass in Florida, several weeks later, we flew home for a second memorial in MA where more than 400 friends and relatives from near and far braced icy conditions; snow and below zero temperatures to pay their final respects to this amazing woman—Mom.

My comfort comes in knowing that mom left a great legacy; her children and grandchildren remain because she lived a blessed life. No one is perfect; we are humans after all that is part of the gift of wisdom she bestowed upon us all.

Mom I miss you, but know that until we meet again, you are among the angels keeping watch over all of us. And, as your care and comfort guided me to adulthood, I feel so blessed to have had the opportunity to care for you in your final hours and in your final journey.

Mom, I love you.

I'll Never Forget You

by MEGHAN SHEA

Granddaughter to Eileen and niece of Paula Camposano Robinson

A grandmother
A mother
A woman loved by many,
Love, Trust, Compassion, a Friendship
My Grandmother could give any

Eileen Camposano was a very good wife,
And a wonderful mother, who led a good life

My grandmother's life was unexpectedly taken,
Leaving my heart
Feeling very shaken

The last time I saw her was on Thanksgiving Day,
God knew I loved her,
So why did he take her away?

Not a day will go by,
Without a thought of her,
I wish my Grandmother was back home again,
Just as things were

I'LL NEVER FORGET YOU

Sometimes life is cruel
Taking the ones we love away,
But I know I'll see her again,
Somehow, someday

She won't be far from my mind,
My thoughts or my heart
For my grandmother was truly a piece of art.

Not one person was like her, she was unique in every way,
I hope to see her in heaven, when I pass away.

Grammy I love you
I wish I could have said it one last time.
But I know in my heart.
You will always be mine.

I hope you won't forget me,
There is not one thing I'll forget about you
I hope you can hear this Grammy "I love you"
As Thanksgiving will forever come, I will be reminded of all of the fun,
And truly be thankful
For all the things we have done.

Priceless Caregiving
RESOURCES AND INFORMATION

Choosing Home Care Services

by VALERIE VANBOOVEN, RN, BSN

- Be organized.
- Ask the Home Care Agency if they have a back-up person on-call in case of caregivers becoming ill or not showing up.
- Provide the aide with a checklist of duties for EACH DAY.
- The aide should not sleep or smoke in your home.
- If there is a problem, immediately contact the agency that sent the aide.
- The aides should provide their own lunch/dinner unless you offer.
- Do not tip.
- Do not send your loved one out in a car with the aide unless this situation is prearranged with the agency.
- Aides should only *minimally* use the phone for personal calls.
- Make sure you know in advance how payment is expected.
- Some aides are Certified Nurse's Aides (CNAs) and others are not. Some will take a blood pressure and a pulse, while others will not. Ask the agency.
- There should be some consistency after about 1 to 2 weeks regarding the person who is sent to the home. Sometimes it takes a week or so to get the same person on the schedule for your home. Be patient!
- What is the hiring practice of the agency? Have background checks been performed on every caregiver? What about Elder Abuse or Child Abuse database checks? Are they bonded and insured?

- If there are too many late shows/no shows or inconsistencies, CHANGE AGENCIES (speak to them about the problem first, perhaps they can correct the situation).

MEDICAL VS. NON-MEDICAL HOME CARE SERVICES

There are two different types of home care providers, *medical* and *non-medical.* A non-medical home care agency supplies caregivers who will do household chores such as light cleaning, laundry, errand running, grocery shopping, picking up prescriptions, light meal preparation, and getting the mail. They will also provide services that help with socialization and transportation like accompanying the aging adult to a doctor's appointment, sitting and watching TV together, playing card games or board games, taking the senior to special events or senior centers, going to the library, and other social activities. Again, transporting the senior in the caregiver's vehicle should be pre-approved.

Medical home care providers can assist with many of these things, but also provide bathing and dressing assistance, medication reminders, and assistance with transferring from the bed to a chair.

No one can take care of your parent or spouse exactly the way you would, but a good agency will provide caring and compassionate staff who do the best job they possibly can. The squeaky wheel always gets the grease when it comes to service providers. Do your homework prior to hiring an agency, and be sure to check on your aging loved one regularly. Visit unexpectedly and monitor what's happening in the home. Speak up and communicate with the agency!

Adult Day Services

by VALERIE VANBOOVEN, RN, BSN

ADULT DAY SERVICES ARE BECOMING A POPULAR ALTERNATIVE TO NURSING home placement. They offer the ability for the elderly to spend the day in an enriching environment, full of social activities and learning opportunities, while interacting with others. Many Adult Day Centers will provide transportation to and from the center for an extra charge. Meals are provided, as well as medication administration. Day trips, crafts, computer stations, libraries, and music are often part of the overall experience. Some Adult Day Centers will take Medicaid, but most prefer private pay or long-term care insurance. This allows the senior to live at home with another member of the family, but have supervision and social interaction during the day while family members are at work.

TIPS FOR CHOOSING AN ADULT DAY CARE CENTER

- Identify services in your area. For names and phone numbers of the Adult Day Centers, try:
- Yellow Pages ("Adult Day Care;" "Aging Services;" Senior Citizens' Services," etc.).
- Area Agency on Aging (AAA). Call 1-800-677-1116 for the AAA in your area, or search for them online.
  - A local senior center.
  - Your family doctor.
  - A Geriatric Care Manager.

- Call first! Call Adult Day Centers and ask for a flier or brochure, eligibility criteria, a monthly activity calendar, a monthly menu and application procedures.
- Know what to ask. Look for the following information:
  - Owner or sponsoring agency.
  - Years of operation.
  - Openings and availability. Are they accepting new clients?
  - License or certification (if required in your state).
  - Hours of operation.
  - Days open.
  - Transportation.
  - Cost—Hourly or daily charge, other charges, financial assistance.
  - Medical conditions accepted—such as memory loss, limited mobility, and incontinence.
  - Staff credentials.
  - Number of staff per participant.
  - Activities provided—Is there variety and choice of individual and group activities?
  - Menu—appeal, balance.
- Tour. After reviewing materials, make an appointment to visit two or more centers that might meet your needs.
- Check references. Talk to two or three people who have used the center you are considering. Ask for their opinion.
- Try it out. Select a day center. Try it for three to five days. It sometimes takes several visits for new participants to feel comfortable in a new setting and with a new routine. If you have questions or are experiencing any problems, ask for a conference. The staff may have suggestions to make the transition easier both at home and at the day center.

Hiring a Geriatric Care Manager (Elder Care Manager)

by VALERIE VANBOOVEN, RN, BSN

WHEN FACED WITH DECISIONS REGARDING LONG-TERM CARE FOR AN AGING loved one, a geriatric care manager may be one of the best private resources in your area. A geriatric care manager has extensive knowledge of all local resources related to aging and caregiving, as well as family and personal issues and concerns.

Geriatric care managers can be located nationwide. They assist with coordination of care for aging and disabled adults. This service is provided in a series of steps including initial assessment, care plan development, implementation of services, and quality of care monitoring. Geriatric care managers are typically nurses, social workers, gerontologists, physical therapists, occupational therapists, or other social service professionals.

The "care management" process can improve the quality of life not only for the aging adult, but also for the caregivers and family members involved. The service is very personalized and utilizes the same principals of "case management."

Most geriatric care managers are available to the family and client 24 hours per day, 7 days per week. The ultimate goal is to keep the aging adult in the home for as long as *safely* possible. In-home care can be arranged at any level of need to accommodate the client and the family. Geriatric care managers often will be asked to arrange other services for the client such as bill paying, housekeeping, lawn care, transportation to appointments, grocery shopping, meal delivery, and personal care issues.

When the client is in need of transition to alternative living arrangements like nursing home, assisted living, or even independent retirement communities, the care manager often can recommend the best facilities that meet the clients financial needs.

Geriatric Care Management is truly a holistic approach to caring for the aging adult. All resources available are utilized to assist families when long-term care is needed.

Care managers are also often asked to troubleshoot quality concerns with nursing homes and home care agencies. Their level of professionalism and knowledge of the local regulations and laws are of great value to the family. They are considered "advocates" for the elderly.

Geriatric care management is paid for privately by client and family members. Medicare and Medicaid do not cover these services. However, Long-Term Care Insurance does cover some or all of the care management fee.

Most geriatric care managers belong to the National Association of Professional Geriatric Care Managers. In order to find a care manager in your area, you can search for one through their website at *www.caremanager.org.*

Geriatric care management services save the family both time and money, and ultimately decrease the stress and frustration of the caregiver. The process gives the family and the aging adult the opportunity to make informed and appropriate decisions regarding any long-term care needs.

RECOMMENDATIONS FOR CHOOSING A GERIATRIC CARE MANAGER

Choosing a geriatric care manager is much like choosing any other professional that you and your family would be working with closely.

- Look for a member of the National Association of Professional Geriatric Care Managers. These members have met certain criteria regarding education and experience in health sciences and social service.
- Ask for References.
- Ask for literature about their company, years of practice, websites, and biography.

- Check with the Better Business Bureau.
- Ask about fees, contracts, and extra charges like mileage or phone calls.
- Be sure you understand what services they provide and their on-call schedule. Will they be available 24 hours a day?
- Remember that a geriatric care manager becomes your "eyes and ears," especially when you live some distance from your parents. Ask them about their process, their communication schedule (Will they report daily, weekly, or monthly?). Is the primary communication via telephone or email?
- Communicate any concerns immediately, and work together as a team to accomplish the ultimate goal, which is keeping your loved one safe and well cared for.

MY PARENT DOESN'T WANT ANY HELP, WHAT SHOULD I DO?

Perhaps you have noticed that Mom or Dad isn't bathing regularly, or the bills aren't being paid, or the house is uncharacteristically messy. Maybe they seem to forget directions from one location to another, or even worse, they have had a car accident, or report falling in the home when no one was around to help them. Often adult children of aging parents notice changes in their loved ones, and when the aging adult is confronted with the facts, they say, "Oh everything is fine, I don't need any help, don't worry about me!"

The loss of independence and choice is something no one wants to face. Having one's own children tell their parents what do to or how to live their lives is uncomfortable at best. Many aging adults are also very private about their financial matters, and will not discuss income, expenses, or assets with adult children.

HOW DOES AN ADULT CHILD START THAT CONVERSATION WITH THEIR PARENTS?

There is not a one-size-fits-all answer. Below are some tips that might help the process along.

- Choose an appropriate time and place. Avoid large family gatherings, holidays, birthdays, and other celebrations. A quiet location, in their home or yours, might be more comfortable.
- Avoid blaming or accusing. Instead, redirect the conversation by telling your parent how YOU feel. For example, "Mom, I find myself worrying about you a lot these days, and I would like to tell you why I am feeling this way."
- Talk to a geriatric care manager in your area for some good advice on how to approach your parent's specific needs. That care manager has helped family members have this kind of conversation hundreds of times throughout their career. They are full of helpful hints and tips.
- If you decide to seek the services of a geriatric care manager, ask them about their approach when it comes to dealing with difficult clients or clients who may not perceive a need for services.
- Advice for adult children when approaching their parents about setting up an evaluation, might include telling their parents, "I know you don't want me to worry about you, and I only want the best for you. Having this professional come over and talk to us would really make me feel better. If you would agree to talk with her, we can look at her recommendations together and see if any of them make sense. Is that fair?"
- Remember that having a third party, who is not a family member and is completely objective, can help the senior see things from a different point of view. They feel like they are getting some professional advice as opposed to opinions from their children.
- Finally, if the senior is truly not living safely, a geriatric care manager can let the senior know that they need to make some choices about their care or living arrangements NOW, before someone else has to make that decision for them later. Of course this is done with professionalism, courtesy, compassion and caring.

When the Caregiver Needs a Break... Where Can They Turn?

by VALERIE VANBOOVEN, RN, BSN

ONE OUT OF FOUR FAMILIES IN THE U.S. TODAY ARE CARING FOR AN AGING adult in some way. For some families that means 24-hour live-in care. For other families that means that Mom needs a ride to the doctor or to the grocery.

In the next 10-20 years it is projected that elder care will replace childcare as the number one issue for working adults. Employers will likewise be affected.

Caring for an aging parent can be rewarding and overwhelming at the same time. After all, these are ones parents who raised us and cared for us. It's very difficult when the roles reverse.

Respite (*res-* pit) care is often the answer. Respite care is *time off* for the caregiver. Respite gives the caregiver time away to rest and do necessary activities so that they can continue to provide good care for their loved one. Often being a caregiver is a job that can be physically and emotionally draining. Without relief a person's physical and emotional health can be affected, reducing the quality of care for their family member. There are several options when it comes to respite care.

In-home care can be arranged for as little as a few hours, up to several days with the proper planning and financial resources. Be sure to pick an agency with a great reputation and proven reliability. Make sure that background checks are done on all employees and Elder/Child Abuse checks are also completed. In-home care for long periods of time can be costly, so be sure to budget for the expense. Also many home health agencies require several days or weeks of advance notice for long assignments. Plan ahead!

Nursing Home/Assisted Living facilities often will offer respite care for a weekend or a full week or more. Many facilities have a minimum number of days required. The cost includes room and board. Many other services will be extra. Some facilities will only require a few days notice, and others will require several weeks notice. Check with the facilities in your area for costs and bed availability. Again, as always it is important to plan ahead.

Local Area Agencies on Aging or Social Service Agencies will sometimes sponsor programs that allow for volunteers to come to the home and provide respite care for short periods of time. These visits are usually just for a few hours. The volunteers are not medical professionals and therefore are not able to care for seriously ill family members, but they are able to provide some relief! These programs are usually free or at a very low cost to local residents. Contact your local Area Agency on Aging for more information.

The Alzheimer's Association is a great source of information. It is not necessary to be taking care of an Alzheimer's diagnosed family member to take advantage of their referral database. Your local agency can usually provide you with a wealth of information, resources and contacts.

Family and friends are a great resource for the caregiver. Don't be afraid to ask for help. Many people are happy to assist with errand running and caregiving. Have a family meeting and ask each family member for 1-2 hours of his or her time per week. This will allow the caregiver to take a hot bath, read a book, go for a much-needed walk, or just go shopping. Make a schedule and give each family member a copy.

Local Churches and Other Organizations are generally willing to send volunteers out to the home for a few hours. Again, most of these volunteers are non-medical personnel and will only be able to stay for a couple of hours at a time.

Taking care of yourself is just as important as caring for your disabled/ aging family member. If you become ill, what will happen to your loved one? Don't hesitate to ask for help. If you look in the right places you might find more help than you need.

So take a much-needed break. You deserve it!

HOSPICE CARE—AT THE END OF LIFE

Hospice care is end of life care. Usually it is estimated by a physician that a patient has 6 months or less to live. Hospice focuses on caring for the individual, keeping them comfortable, and providing support for the family. Hospice care can be provided in the home, in a designated hospice facility, or in a long-term care facility. These services are available to patients of all ages. It is covered under Medicare, Medicaid, and most private insurance plans. Long-Term Care Insurance also covers hospice care.

The primary caregiver for a hospice patient is usually a family member. There is a team of healthcare professionals available to help the primary caregiver. This team often includes a physician, a registered nurse, home health aids, clergy or social services, trained volunteers, and physical or occupational therapists. Traditional insurance plans like Medicare and private health insurance will cover needed supplies, equipment, and licensed healthcare practitioners like nurses and physical therapists. However when a family needs 24 hour care provided by a home health aid, or other unlicensed personnel, they end up paying privately for this service or utilize their long-term care insurance benefits. Most long-term care insurers provide hospice care as a standard benefit in their plan and there is no need to meet the waiting period (elimination period).

Pay Yourself or a Loved One for Providing Care— The Options and Tax Benefits

by VALERIE VANBOOVEN, RN, BSN

MANY ADULT CHILDREN FIND IT FINANCIALLY IMPOSSIBLE TO LEAVE THEIR CURrent employer and give up a much needed salary to take care of an aging adult. There are some ways to offset that financial responsibility, but it does take diligence and investigation the part of the adult child.

Seniors can pay adult children or other care providers just like they would a home health agency for services. *Increasing cash flow for the senior to afford to pay privately for care can be done through a reverse mortgage.*

Some seniors have *long-term care insurance* that allows a family member to be the primary caregiver, and get reimbursed for providing the care.

IF NEITHER OF THOSE OPTIONS APPLY, HERE ARE SOME OTHER OPTIONS:

- If employed, check with you company's human resource department or seek the counsel of your employee assistance program to find out about family leave options or local programs that assist with caregiving expenses and options.
- Contact Eldercare Locator, as service of the National Association of Area Agencies on Aging at *www.n4a.org/locator* or phone 800-677-1116.

- A state by state listing of paid leave programs for caregivers can be found at *www.paidfamilyleave.org*

SOME OTHER EXAMPLES THAT OFFER AT LEAST SOME LEVEL OF COMPENSATION FOR CAREGIVING FAMILY MEMBERS INCLUDE:

- *Colorado:* In rural areas, family members providing assistance to loved ones may be eligible to receive up to $400 per month as compensation to provide personal care services.
- *North Dakota* pays up to $700 per month to spouses and other family members who care for Medicaid beneficiaries living in rural areas who would otherwise require admission to a nursing home.
- *Wisconsin:* A family member may be eligible for compensation either for caregiving or, in some situations, for performing services normally provided by a social worker.
- *North Carolina*: Family caregivers supporting loved ones may be able to reduce out of pocket expenses through the use of state-funded vouchers that can be used to buy nutritional supplements, incontinence supplies, and personal emergency response systems, among other items. In some circumstances caregivers may be eligible for direct cash compensation. While in most cases compensation is provided to family members who are not immediate family, there are times when immediate family is eligible for pay, such as when they are caring for a loved one with dementia who lives in a rural area.
- *Massachusetts:* Elders who meet Medicaid criteria and who qualify for nursing home care now have the option of receiving compensated home-based care from family members or friends. The Enhanced Adult Foster Program covers up to $18,000 annually for family members who provide 24-hour care in the home. These caregivers receive specialized training, support of both a registered nurse and a care manager, and help in locating respite services.

TAX DEDUCTIONS AND BENEFITS FOR CAREGIVERS

There are certain criteria that must be met if a family caregiver is planning to claim an aging parent as a dependent.

1. You must provide more than half of a person's financial support.
2. The dependent may be a relative or non-relative living with you for the entire year or residing in a nursing home or assisted living home.
3. They (the dependent) must be a citizen of the U.S., Canada, or Mexico.
4. The dependent must not file a joint tax return for the same year.
5. The dependent must have less than $3,200 of gross annual income. Social Security benefits and tax exempt interest income are not included in this equation (neither would reverse mortgage proceeds, as they are not taxable).

QUALIFYING EXPENSES INCLUDE:

1. medications
2. long-term care insurance premiums
3. home modifications
4. transportation for medical appointments
5. services of privately hired in-home care workers
6. spending for wheelchairs, eye glasses, and dentures
7. Look for anything related to meeting the long-term care needs of the individual! Any expense not covered by insurance may be eligible for deductions.
8. For those residing in an assisted living facility, there may be a certain percentage allowed as deductible.
9. For those residing in a nursing home—and *paying privately* for their care, the cost is fully deductible.

It's important to consult the advice of a tax advisor or elder law attorney, especially if the support gets complicated—for instance:

- When multiple siblings contribute to the support of a parent.
- When taxable income could be moved into tax-free investments
- When there is the possibility that the dependent may need to apply for Medicaid.
- When a caregiver contract is desired to provide family members with compensation for services, housing, etc.

If you hired someone to care for your loved one while you either sought or maintained employment, you may qualify for the Child and Dependent Care Credit. Depending on your income, this credit may equal up to 35% of your qualifying expenses. To claim the credit, the following conditions must be met:

- You must have earned income wages, salaries, tips, employee compensation or net earnings from self-employment.
- Payments for care cannot be made to any person you claim as a dependent or to your child under age 19.
- You must file as single, head of household, qualified widow(er) with a dependent child, or married filing jointly.
- The care must have been provided by a qualifying individual.
- The dependent must have lived with you for more than half of the year.

Remember to consult a local tax consultant for more help, information, and possible state level deductions in your area.

TALK TO EMPLOYERS ABOUT DEPENDENT CARE FSAS

Consider utilizing a Dependent Care FSA (Flexible Spending Accounts) to help pay for medical/elder care expenses. These plans allow employees to contribute a portion of salary, before taxes, to accounts designated for health care expenses, including premiums and child/elder care expenses. Then employees are reimbursed from their accounts with tax free dollars for unreimbursed medical expenses and child/elder care expenses. The funds must be used before the end of the plan year, or grace period, or else unused dollars are forfeited. If a caregiver has access to these plans, they should use them, but plan carefully so that contributions are not more than can be used in a year.

If an elderly parent lives with a participant and relies on that person for at least 50% of their support, then the Dependent Care FSA may be used for day care expenses. However, the care must be necessary to allow the participant to work, and cannot be custodial nursing care. Also, if the participant is married, the care must be necessary because the spouse also works, is looking for work or is a full-time student.

Choosing Independent Senior Living, Assisted Living, and Nursing Home Care

by VALERIE VANBOOVEN, RN, BSN

A Continuum of Care Retirement Community or CCRC is a community for seniors that encompasses all levels of care, from independent living, to assisted living, to nursing home care, all on one campus. Some couples and single seniors will move to a CCRC for various reasons including simplifying their lifestyle, no longer having to worry about lawn and house maintenance, and increased social activity with people of their own generation. Independent living offers an apartment or town-home with access to 1-2 meals per day in a restaurant style setting, recreational activities, group tours and day outings, and transportation to doctor appointments and grocery stores. They often include walking trails, workout rooms, arts and crafts areas, computer labs, libraries, chapels, and small convenience stores. The independent portion of a CCRC is not considered long-term care; it is simply a lifestyle choice. Independent senior living has a cost range of $1100-$5000 per month. Most cities do have Section 8 or HUD housing specifically for seniors. Sometimes there is a waiting list for subsidized housing.

ASSISTED LIVING FACILITIES

Sometimes, on the same campus there are assisted living facilities that offer most of the same accommodations, but with a little more assistance and structure. In an assisted living facility each resident typically has their own apartment, but without a kitchenette. They are served 3 meals per day in a family style or restaurant style setting. Medication delivery is available, as well as linen service, laundry service, housekeeping, and assistance with bathing and dressing if needed. Again, recreational and social activities, and transportation are also provided.

There are stand-alone assisted living facilities that are not associated with CCRCs. Assisted living is becoming the most popular form of long-term care, and is seen as a transition between independent living and nursing home care. This is a nice option for people who need some extra help but are not ready for full 24-hour care. Cost for Assisted Living ranges from $1900-$5000 per month and can be paid for with private funds or long-term care insurance. Occasionally in some states Assisted Living Facilities can accept Medicaid.

NURSING HOME CARE

When independent or assisted living is no longer a viable option, a nursing home will provide 24-hour care by trained and licensed staff. A Registered Nurse or Licensed Practical Nurse is on duty at all times. Some nursing homes are private pay only, some take Medicare, and some will accept Medicaid as payment for services. Most residents live in a semi-private room (private if they can afford it), and are allowed to decorate with their own personal belongings. There are new trends in nursing home care called The Eden Alternative ™. These programs incorporate living things like plants, animals, and children into residential care facilities to make them more like a home, rather than an institution for the frail and elderly. The average cost for a semi-private nursing home bed nationwide in 2007 is around $206.00 per day ($6180 per month) or more.

TIPS FOR CHOOSING AN ASSISTED LIVING OR NURSING CARE FACILITY

Choosing a facility for a loved one, or even for yourself, can be difficult and time consuming. The following tips and hints will help give you guidance when trying to make that decision. Remember—take notes on each facility you visit and compare them later.

- Speak with people you trust about their experiences with Nursing Homes.
- Pick a good LOCATION.
- Ask the home about BED AVAILABILITY.
- Do they have Medicare, Medicaid, or private pay beds available?
- What is the STAFFING ARRANGEMENT? RNS? LPNS? CNAS?
- Are there extra services and fees?
- Is the home able to provide for special care needs such as Alzheimer's, End Stage Renal Disease, or other medical conditions?
- VISIT THE HOMES ON YOUR LIST! Nothing replaces a tour.
- Ask to see a copy of the most recent state inspection. Or visit the Nursing Home Compare site on the web at *www.medicare.gov*.
- Do the residents seem to have a good quality of life?
- How long has the current staff been working at the facility?
- Does the facility conduct background checks for criminal and elder abuse activity prior to hiring employees?
- Upon entering the facility, pay attention to what you SEE and what you SMELL.
- What are the visiting hours?
- Security? Safety plans for fire evacuations etc?
- Be sure to visit the home at least once when they are not expecting you.
- Make an inventory of the items that you or your loved one brings to the home for future reference.
- Talk to some of the other visitors/ family members. How do they feel about the care provided?

Resources Online and Offline

by VALERIE VANBOOVEN, RN, BSN

REVERSE MORTGAGE INFORMATION AND SERVICES

NATIONAL REVERSE MORTGAGE LENDERS ASSOCIATION
1400 16th St., NW, Suite 420
Washington, DC 20036
PHONE: 202.939.1760
WEBSITE: *www.nrmla.org*

LIFE SETTLEMENTS

LIFE SETTLEMENT PRO
202 Lonesome Pine Dr.
Longwood, FL 32779
TOLL FREE: 888.973.8377
EFAX: 206.333.0112
WEBSITE: *www.lifesettlementpro.com*

LONG-TERM CARE INSURANCE/ HEALTH INSURANCE

LTC GLOBAL CORPORATE OFFICES
33 North Central Avenue, Suite 317
Medford, Oregon 97501-5939
TOLL FREE: 800.362.8837
FAX: 541.245.9700
WEBSITE: *www.ltcglobal.com*

NATIONAL ASSOCIATION OF INSURANCE COMMISSIONERS—NAIC
Hall of States
444 North Capitol Street, NW, Suite 701
Washington, DC 20001-1512
PHONE: 202.624.7790
WEBSITE: *www.naic.org*

HEALTH INSURANCE ASSOCIATION OF AMERICA, PUBLIC AFFAIRS DEPARTMENT—HIAA
555 13th St., NW, Suite 600
Washington, DC 20004
PHONE: 202.824.1600
WEBSITE: *www.hiaa.org*

AMERICAN ASSOCIATION FOR LONG-TERM CARE INSURANCE
AALTCI
3835 E. Thousand Oaks Blvd., Suite 336
Westlake Village, CA 91362
PHONE: 818.597.3227
WEBSITE: *www.aaltci.org*

THE CENTER FOR LONG-TERM CARE REFORM
2212 Queen Anne Ave North #110
Seattle, WA 98109
PHONE: 206.283.7036
WEBSITE: *www.centerltc.org*

GOVERNMENT AGENCIES OF INTEREST

DEPARTMENT OF VETERANS AFFAIRS (VA)
810 Vermont Ave. NW
Washington, DC 20420
PHONE: 800.827.1000
WEBSITE: *www.va.gov*

PARALYZED VETERANS OF AMERICA (PVA)
Veterans Benefits Dept.
801 18th St., NW
Washington, DC 20006
PHONE: 800.424.8200
WEBSITE: *www.pva.org*

CENTERS FOR MEDICARE & MEDICAID SERVICES (CMS)

Region VII
Richard Bolling Federal Building
601 East 12th Street, Room 235
Kansas City, Missouri 64106
PHONE: 800.MEDICARE
WEBSITE: *www.medicare.gov*

200 Independence Avenue, SW, Room 303-D
Washington, DC 20201
TOLL-FREE: 877.267.2323
EMAIL: *question@cms.gov*
WEBSITE: *www.cms.gov*

AREA AGENCIES ON AGING

Eldercare Locator
927 15th St. NW, 6th Floor
Washington, DC 20005
ELDERCARE LOCATOR: 800.677.1116
WEBSITES: *www.n4a.org*
www.eldercare.gov

FIRST GOV FOR SENIORS

WEBSITE: *www.seniors.gov*

NATIONAL INSTITUTE ON AGING

WEBSITE: *www.nih.gov/nia*

NATIONAL COUNCIL ON AGING

1901 L Street, N.W., 4th floor
Washington, D.C. 20036
PHONE: 202.479.1200
TDD: 202.479.6674
EMAIL: *info@ncoa.org*
WEBSITE: *www.ncoa.org*

LEGAL RESOURCES

COMMISSION ON LEGAL PROBLEMS OF THE ELDERLY

WEBSITE: *www.abanet.org/elderly*

NATIONAL ACADEMY OF ELDER LAW ATTORNEYS
1604 N Country Club Road
Tucson, AZ 85716
WEBSITE: *www.naela.org*

SENIORLAW
WEBSITE: *www.seniorlaw.com*

CAREGIVER RESOURCES: HOME CARE AND ADULT DAY CARE

NATIONAL ADULT DAY SERVICES ASSOCIATION, INC.
8201 Greensboro Drive, Suite 300
McLean, Virginia 22102
PHONE: 703.610.9035
TOLL-FREE: 866.890.7357
EMAIL: *info@nadsa.org*
PHONE: *www.nadsa.org*

NATIONAL ASSOCIATION FOR HOME CARE
228 7th Street, SE
Washington, DC 20003
PHONE: 202.547.7424
WEBSITE: *www.nahc.org*

ABLEDATA—ASSISTIVE DEVICES
8630 Fenton Street, Suite 930
Silver Spring, MD 20910
PHONE: 800.227.0216
TTY: 301.608.8912
WEBSITE: *www.abledata.com*

MEALS ON WHEELS ASSOCIATION OF AMERICA
WEBSITE: *www.mowaa.org*

CAREGIVER RESOURCES: HOSPICE

PARTNERSHIP FOR CARING
1620 Eye Street NW, Suite 202
Washington, DC 20006
PHONE: 202.296.8071
HOTLINE: 800.989.9455
WEBSITE: *www.caringinfo.org*

HOSPICE FOUNDATION OF AMERICA
2001 S St. NW #300
Washington DC 20009
PHONE: 800.854.3402
WEBSITE: *www.hospicefoundation.org*

NATIONAL HOSPICE & PALLIATIVE CARE ORGANIZATION (NHPCO)
1700 Diagonal Road, Suite 625
Alexandria, Virginia 22314
Phone: 703.837.1500
THE NHPCO HELPLINE: 800.658.8898
WEBSITE: *www.nhpco.org*

RESOURCES FOR CAREGIVERS: HOUSING

THE ASSISTED LIVING FEDERATION OF AMERICA
11200 Waples Mill Rd, Suite 150
Fairfax, VA 22030
PHONE: 703.691.8100
EMAIL: *info@alfa.org*
WEBSITE: *www.alfa.org*

NATIONAL SHARED HOUSING RESOURCE CENTER
National Center for Assisted Living-NCAL
1201 L Street, NW
Washington, DC 20005
PHONE: 202.842.4444
WEBSITE: *www.ncal.org*
WEBSITE: *www.nationalsharedhousing.org*

AMERICAN ASSOCIATION OF HOMES AND SERVICES FOR THE AGING—AAHSA
2519 Connecticut Ave. NW
Washington, DC 20008
PHONE: 800.508.9442
WEBSITE: *www.aahsa.org*
The Eden Alternative™
WEBSITE: *www.edenalt.com*

CAREGIVER RESOURCES: GERIATRIC CARE MANAGEMENT

NATIONAL ASSOCIATION OF PROFESSIONAL GERIATRIC CARE MANAGERS
1604 N Country Club Road
Tucson, AZ 85716 USA
WEBSITE: *www.caremanager.org*

CAREGIVER RESOURCES: MEDICATIONS

AMERICAN PHARMACEUTICAL ASSOCIATION—APHA
2215 Constitution Avenue, NW
Washington, DC 20037-2985
TOLL-FREE: 800-237-APHA
EMAIL: *mail@aphanet.org*
WEBSITE: *www.aphanet.org*

CENTER WATCH—CLINICAL DRUG TRIALS LISTINGS
WEBSITE: *www.centerwatch.com*

MEDLINEPLUS
WEBSITE: *www.nlm.nih.gov/medlineplus*

CAREGIVER RESOURCES: FINDING DOCTORS

AMERICAN MEDICAL ASSOCIATION—AMA
515 North State Street
Chicago, IL 60610
PHONE: 312.464.4818
EMAIL: *amalibrary@ama-assn.org*
WEBSITE: *www.ama-assn.org*

GERONTOLOGICAL SOCIETY OF AMERICA
WEBSITE: *www.geron.org*

CAREGIVER RESOURCES: CAREGIVER ORGANIZATIONS AND SUPPORT

CHILDREN OF AGING PARENTS
1609 Woodbourne Road, Suite 302A
Levittown, PA 19057 USA
PHONE: 800.277.7294
WEBSITE: *www.caps4caregivers.org*

NATIONAL FAMILY CAREGIVERS ASSOCIATION
10400 Connecticut Avenue, #500
Kensington, MD 20895-3944
PHONE: 800.896.3650
WEBSITE: *www.nfcacares.org*

THE WELL SPOUSE FOUNDATION
63 West Main Street, Suite H
Freehold, NJ 07728
PHONE: 800.838.0879
WEBSITE: *www.wellspouse.org*

OTHER CAREGIVER SITES OF INTEREST:
www.caregiving.com
www.caregiver.com
www.carescout.com
http://griefnet.org

SENIOR ADVOCACY AND INTEREST GROUPS

NATIONAL CONSUMERS LEAGUE
1701 K Street, NW, Suite 1200
Washington, DC 20006
Phone: 202.835.3323
WEBSITE: *www.natlconsumersleague.org*

FAMILIES USA
WEBSITE: *www.familiesusa.org*

ELDERWEB
WEBSITE: *www.elderweb.com*

UNITED SENIORS HEALTH COUNCIL—USHC
409 3rd St., SW, Suite 200
Washington, DC 20024
PHONE: 202.479.6673
WEBSITE: *www.unitedseniorshealth.org*

AMERICAN HEALTH CARE ASSOCIATION
1201 L Street, N.W.
Washington, DC 20005
PHONE: 202.842.4444
WEBSITE: *www.ahca.org*

ALLIANCE FOR RETIRED AMERICANS
888 16th St., N.W., Suite 520
Washington, D.C. 20006
PHONE: 888.373.6497
WEBSITE: *www.retiredamericans.org*

AMERICAN SOCIETY ON AGING—ASA
833 Market Street, Suite 511
San Francisco, CA 94103
PHONE: 415.974.9600
EMAIL: *info@asaging.org*
WEBSITE: *www.asaging.org*

ALLIANCE FOR AGING RESEARCH
2021 K Street, NW, Suite 305
Washington, DC 20006
PHONE: 800.639.2421
EMAIL: *info@agingresearch.org*
WEBSITE: *www.agingresearch.org*

AARP
WEBSITE: *www.aarp.org*

BENEFITS CHECK-UP
WEBSITE: *www.benefitscheckup.org*

MISCELLANEOUS SITES OF INTEREST

MAYO CLINIC
WEBSITE: *www.mayohealth.org*

ON HEALTH
WEBSITE: *www.webmd.com*

SPECIFIC DISEASE PROCESSES AND ORGANIZATIONS ON-LINE:

NATIONAL ALZHEIMER'S ASSOCIATION
WEBSITE: *www.alz.org*

ALZHEIMER'S RESEARCH FORUM
WEBSITE: *www.alzforum.org*

ALZHEIMER'S DISEASE EDUCATION AND REFERRAL
WEBSITE: *www.alzheimers.org*

AMERICAN CANCER SOCIETY
WEBSITE: *www.cancer.org*

AMERICAN DIABETES ASSOCIATION
WEBSITE: *www.diabetes.org*

AMERICAN HEART ASSOCIATION
WEBSITE: *www.americanheart.org*

AMERICAN STROKE ASSOCIATION
A Division of American Heart Association
7272 Greenville Avenue
Dallas, TX 75231
PHONE: 888.4STROKE
EMAIL: *strokeassociation@heart.org*
WEBSITE: *www.strokeassociation.org*

ARTHRITIS FOUNDATION
WEBSITE: *www.arthritis.org*

NATIONAL ORGANIZATION FOR RARE DISORDERS
WEBSITE: *www.rarediseases.org*

NATIONAL ASSOCIATION FOR CONTINENCE
WEBSITE: *www.nafc.org*

NATIONAL OSTEOPOROSIS FOUNDATION
WEBSITE: *www.nof.org*

NATIONAL SLEEP FOUNDATION
WEBSITE: *www.sleepfoundation.org*

PARKINSON'S RESOURCE ORGANIZATION
WEBSITE: *www.parkinsonsresource.org*

SELF HELP FOR HARD OF HEARING PEOPLE
WEBSITE: *www.shhh.org*

LIGHTHOUSE NATIONAL CENTER FOR VISION AND AGING—NCVA
111 East 59th Street
New York, NY 10022
PHONE: 800-829-0500
TDD: 212-821-9713
EMAIL: *info@lighthouse.org*
WEBSITE: *www.lighthouse.org*